sleeping: solved

sleeping: solved

First published in 2009 by
Collins, an imprint of
HarperCollins Publishers
77-85 Fulham Palace Road
London W6 8JB
www.collins.co.uk

Collins is a registered trademark of HarperCollins Publishers Ltd

9 8 7 6 5 4 3 2 1

A catalogue record for this book is available from the British Library

Project Editor: Corinne Roberts
Design: Heike Schüssler and Cooling Brown
Cover Design: Heike Schüssler

ISBN: 978 0 00 728919 6

Colour reproduction by Dot Gradations, Essex
Printed and bound in Hong Kong by Printing Express

Always seek the advice of your general practitioner or other qualified health-care professional regarding any medical condition: the information given in this book should not be treated as a substitute for professional medical advice. Neither the author nor the publisher can be held responsible for any loss or claim as a result of the use, or misuse, of the suggestions made or the failure to take medical advice.

The contents of this book are correct at the time of going to print.

Contents

Foreword

The day after I gave birth to my first daughter, I was sitting in the maternity ward gazing adoringly at my tiny baby when the girl in the next bed, a second-time-around mum, leaned over and said, 'You should talk to your baby, you know, she'll love the sound of your voice and you haven't said anything to her yet. The more you speak to her, the quicker she'll learn to talk.' She was right. I was so busy admiring my new little bundle I hadn't uttered a word to her. I'd forgotten about my new role as her mum. From that moment on I plied the second-time-around-mum with the kind of questions I was too shy to ask the midwife: should my baby's legs be so curled up? Am I breastfeeding correctly? Are her fingers meant to be that purple and why am I so scared that something will happen to her if I go to the loo...

It was out of this constant need for answers that **gurgle.com** was born. I'm not the first mum who arrived home with a tiny baby feeling engulfed by the enormity of the task ahead. It didn't start there, the questions started before I became pregnant: what's ovulation? When will I fall pregnant? Will my morning sickness ever stop? At **gurgle.com** we try to provide parents and parents-to-be with a place they can visit for all those 3am worries, a place where they can see weekly updates of their child's development and above all a place where they can meet other parents going through exactly the same things they are. After all, having a baby is not a journey anyone should do alone.

The more we talked to the mums using **gurgle**, the more we realised that the same questions came up again and again. So we decided to publish a set of **gurgle** books in response to the most asked questions on the site. We want these books to guide you through what mums have told us are the three trickiest areas of parenting: how to enjoy your pregnancy (and we promise you can), getting your baby into good sleep habits, and feeding your baby. We don't want to preach or tell you how it should be done, but we do want to provide you with lots of helpful information and tips based on the advice of both our **gurgle** panel of experts and our incredibly supportive and knowledgeable community of mums.

We want you to see our **gurgle** books as your older sister or best friend who has had a baby and is passing on her knowledge to you. We're the midwife who helps you with breastfeeding, or the auntie who suggests a way to help your baby sleep at night.

As much as I wanted to take my maternity ward 'neighbour' home with me, I couldn't. I had to learn how to become a parent, just as my daughter had to learn to sit, walk and talk. We hope that these books become that tap on the shoulder in the maternity ward giving you a friendly nudge in the right direction. Oh, and just for the record, my daughter is now a right little chatterbox...

Nifa McLaughlin
Editor of **gurgle.com** and mum to Ivy and Poppy

We hope you enjoy our books and if we've missed anything out, please visit **gurgle.com** for lots more videos, groups, articles, chat and tools to complement these books. Register with **gurgle.com** and receive free weekly emails walking you through pregnancy and parenthood.

Sleep, your baby and you

Getting through the first few weeks

Adapting to life with a new baby can be hard work. After a physically tiring nine months of pregnancy, the reality of your dependent little red-faced bundle can, at times, be both daunting and exhausting.

If you have never done it before, you may be reeling from a range of different emotions and feelings: the exhausting, mind-blowing experience that was labour; the bewildering knowledge that your life will never be the same again; and the overwhelming worry that, unlike all the other new mothers on your ward, you have no idea how to get through the next few weeks with just this single-minded, helpless little creature for company.

So, how do you cope? The answer is: a day at a time. Before your baby has adapted to a more settled routine, she will be getting used to the baffling world around her. This means that basic human functions such as sleep operate rather haphazardly for a while. Immediately following the birth, your baby will (thankfully for you) sleep most of the available hours there are for a few days, which offers you a chance to catch up after giving birth. It won't be long, however, before your baby is waking more often and, initially, at seemingly random times.

The 'sleeping through the night' myth

When it comes to sleeping, you will, no doubt, be treated to stories of parents whose babies slept through the night at six weeks old. While this is possible, it is also rare. Small babies have very small tummies and therefore cannot hold lots of food in one go. This is why they need to feed a few times in the night to get through.

'Sleeping through the night' is also a deceptive phrase, as it usually refers to your baby having six hours of uninterrupted sleep. This means that if she falls asleep at 11pm and wakes at 5am, she will have had her night's sleep, even though you haven't. Bear with her for the time being and try to encourage good sleep habits by setting up a routine before she goes to bed (bath, pyjamas, story, lullaby, bed) and try not to feed her back to sleep when she wakes.

The key to your baby sleeping through the night is getting her to soothe herself back to sleep without having to be rocked, fed or sung to, so try putting her down to sleep when she is awake to encourage her to fall asleep on her own. Three-month-old babies need about 14 hours of sleep, which roughly equates to four hours in the day and ten hours at night. These aren't continuous hours of sleep and your baby may nap in two- to three-hour stretches or in a series of smaller naps throughout the day and night.

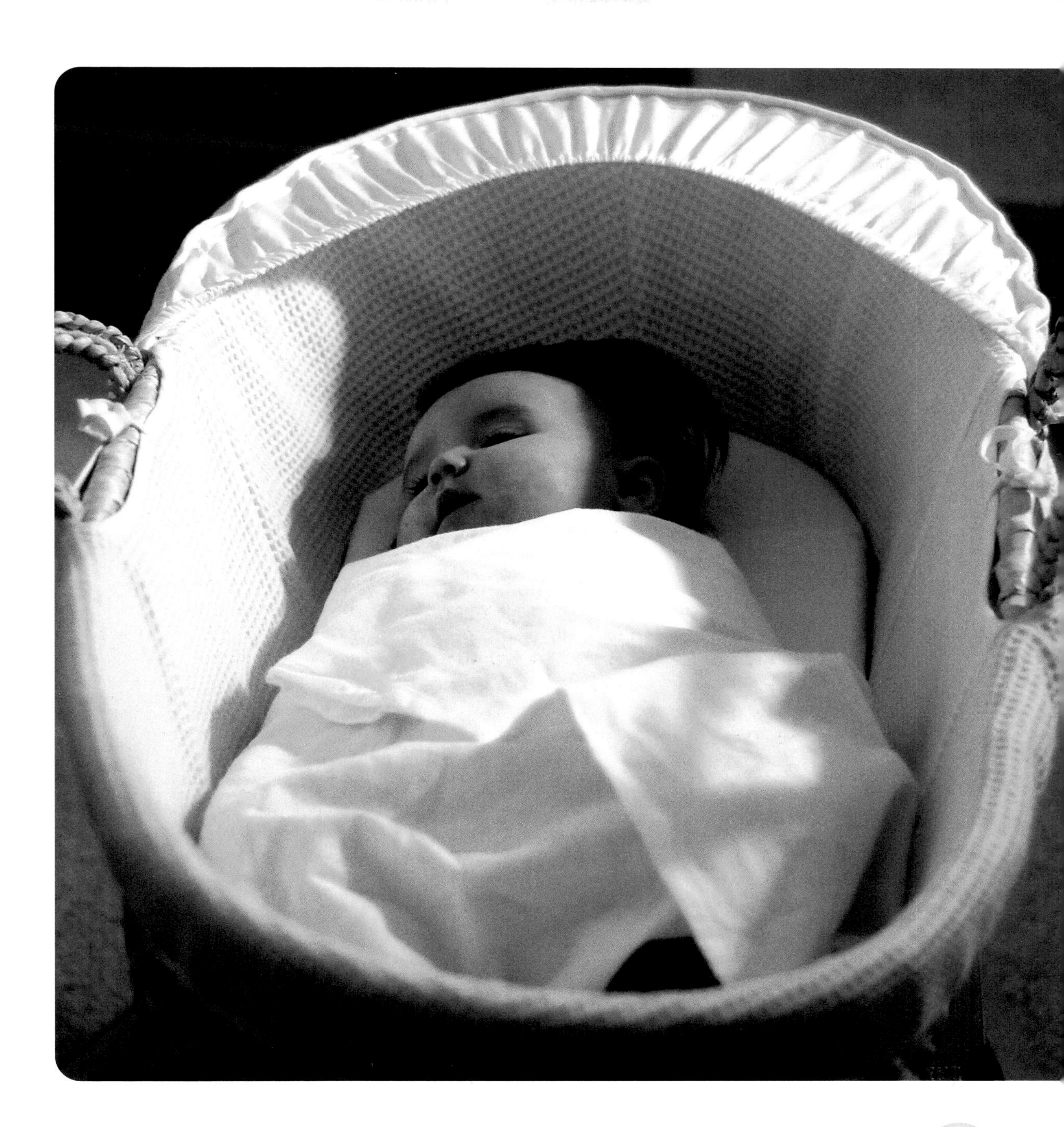

No one – whether baby, toddler, child, teenager or grown-up – is the same when it comes to sleep, so resist the urge to compare your baby's sleep patterns with anyone else's. This is also a very rough estimate as some babies need very little sleep while others are fond of a long slumber. If you are worried about your baby's sleep patterns, consult your health visitor or GP for advice.

Sleep cycles and your baby

Sleep comes in different cycles, which we are hardly aware of but which in fact consist of two pronounced states of consciousness.

- The first is 'dream sleep', or what is referred to as 'rapid eye movement' (REM) sleep, so called because our eyes move quickly under their lids while, apart from the odd twitch, our bodies remain still.

- The second is known as 'deep sleep' or 'non-rapid eye movement' (NREM) sleep, in which we dream relatively little. It is during this phase of sleep that the body repairs itself and the immune system is strengthened.

Newborn babies need nearly twice the amount of sleep that an adult requires and even at 18 months they will still need, on average, five hours more sleep than their parents do. Your baby, when she is newborn, will spend a lot more time in the 'dream sleep' stage, which you can distinguish from the other stages by seeing her twitch occasionally and her eyes moving beneath her lids. When she is in the 'deep sleep' phase of her sleeping cycle, she will make little sucking movements with her mouth and it will be hard to wake her. She may also 'startle' in the same manner that adults do while they are falling asleep. Before the age of three months, your baby won't be able to differentiate between night and day and so her sleep will be scattered across the 24-hour period.

After the three-month stage, your baby will start to learn that night equals a longer period of sleep than the daytime naps that she has been having. As she grows older, you will find her naps become less frequent but more predictable and longer-lasting than those of the early months. By six months, you can reasonably expect more of a settled routine.

Mum's top tip

My baby appeared very restless while sleeping at night. She would shuffle her legs and bang them down on the mattress, then lie still. My health visitor explained the mystery to me. There are two kinds of sleep. The first is rapid eye movement (REM) sleep when the body cannot move, only the eyes. This is when we dream. The other kind of sleep is non-rapid eye movement (NREM), in which the body is able to move again - some people even sleepwalk! Everyone goes through a number of NREM stages then REM then NREM, and so on.

How much sleep does my baby need?

One of the biggest talking points among new parents is how much their babies sleep. While some newborns live up to the old adage of 'sleeping like a baby' and go through the night virtually straight away, others will take a bit longer to settle into a routine and might decide it's much more fun to be nocturnal.

Sleep is something we tend to take for granted before we have children. Then suddenly – finding ourselves deprived of it on a daily basis – it becomes an obsession. But while you may not be getting enough sleep, how can you be sure your baby is? Here are some guidelines for the first three years of his life.

Newborns

Of course every newborn is different, but in those first few weeks of life they all have something in common: they tend to sleep between 16 and 19 hours a day, generally in two- to four-hour stretches. In the early days, babies cannot tell the difference between day and night. And this, coupled with the fact that newborns have small tummies, and so need to eat little and often, can lead to lots of sleepless nights!

Some newborns will sleep for longer periods at a time, and this is perfectly normal unless they are premature or of a low birth weight, in which case you may be advised by your health visitor to wake your baby more regularly for feeds.

By the age of three months, many babies will have settled into more of a routine and, with any luck, will be sleeping in stretches of up to six hours a night.

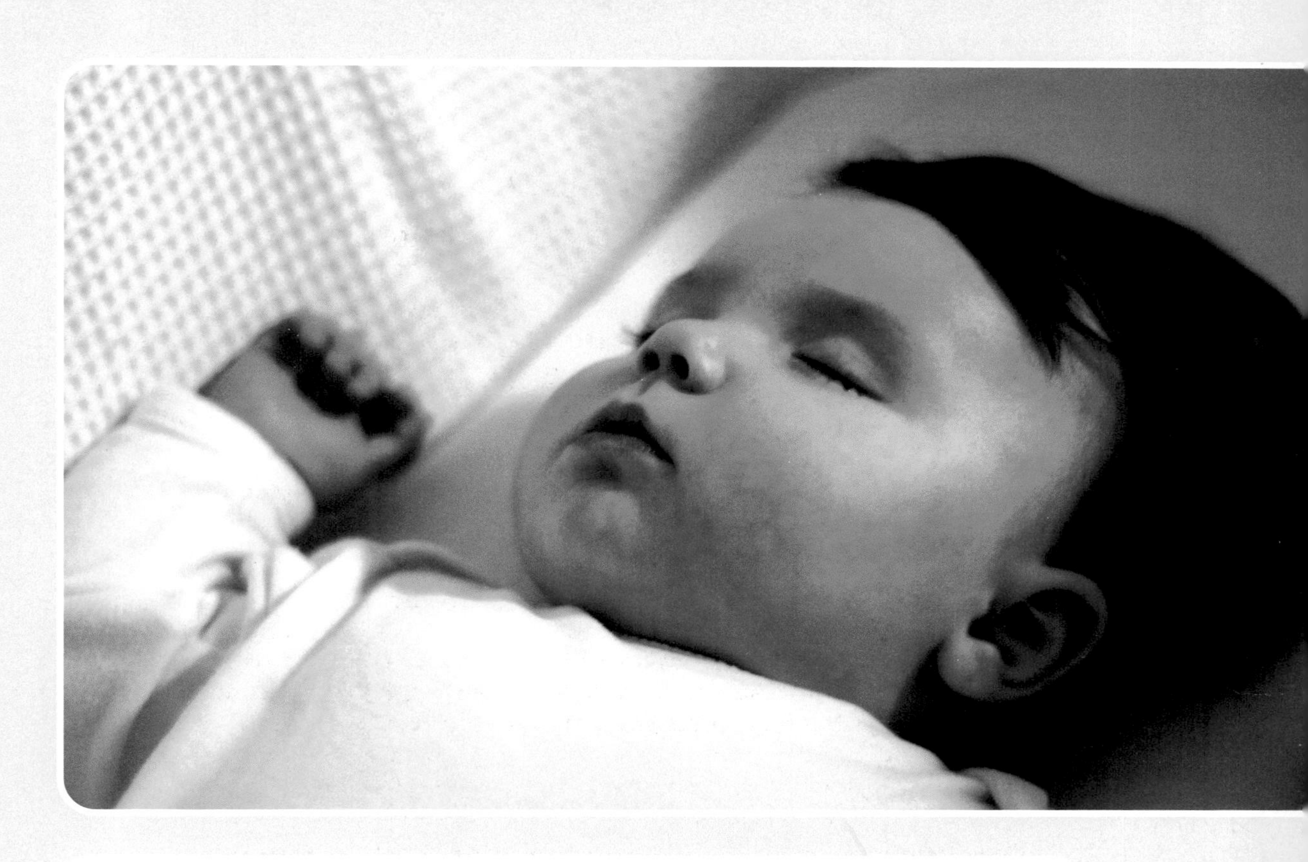

3–12 months

Between the ages of three and six months, as a rule babies will sleep for approximately 14 hours a day, which may be distributed between ten hours at night and four during the day, although don't expect to have an uninterrupted night just yet.

When your baby is between six and 12 months, you may want to think about cutting down his daytime naps to two naps of approximately two hours each. If you're very lucky, your baby may now be sleeping through the night, for 10–12 hours. If you put him to bed at 7pm, he may even sleep through to 7am! This will seem like bliss, but remember that your baby is an individual, and don't worry if he still wakes at night at this age.

Also, don't fall into the trap of thinking that if you put your baby to bed late at night he will be more likely to sleep in late. In fact, the opposite may be true. If your baby doesn't go to bed until 10 or 11pm, he may well be overtired and have a restless and disturbed night's sleep, so try to establish a sensible bedtime routine in the early months, aiming to get your baby in bed by 7pm.

12–18 months

Between the ages of 12 and 18 months, you may decide to reduce your baby's naps still further, especially if you find that he's still waking in the night. As every child is different, there is no hard and fast rule as to how long your one-year-old should sleep, but you may decide that one long afternoon nap of two hours is sufficient.

Two years

When your child reaches the age of two and the toddler years are fully upon you, you may find that he is resistant to going to bed as there are too many exciting things for him to do. You may need to be firm and establish some boundaries. By the age of two, your child should definitely need no more than one nap during the day, of between one and two hours. If you have a bedtime routine firmly in place, he will also - with luck - be sleeping through the night for up to 12 hours!

Three years

By the age of three, your child should need approximately 12 hours' sleep in total. You may decide to cut out his daytime rest altogether or, alternatively, reduce it to one hour-long nap (see pages 124–5 for more about this). You can expect your three-year-old to sleep for about 10–11 hours a night. The benefits of establishing a bedtime routine early on should not be underestimated; the calmer and more settled your child is before going to sleep, the more likely he is to sleep through, so avoid anything that might make him too wound up or excited before going to bed.

Guide to your baby's sleep needs

Remember: every child is different, so the amount of sleep needed will differ from baby to baby. The following chart should serve only as a rough guide.

Age	Night	Day	Total hours of sleep
0–3 months	Spread between night and day		16–19 hours
3–6 months	10 hours	4 hours	14 hours
6–12 months	10–12 hours	2–4 hours	12–14 hours
12–18 months	11–12 hours	1–3 hours	12–14 hours
18–24 months	12 hours	1–2 hours	12–14 hours
2–3 years	12 hours	1 hour (optional)	12 hours

Sleep diary

You may also find it helpful to keep a sleep diary as a record of your baby's sleep patterns. As the name suggests, this is literally a diary in which you can chart everything from how long it takes your baby to settle at bedtime to how many times he wakes in the night, how long he is awake on each occasion and what time he wakes up in the morning. This could be a useful guide for you, as it will help you get a clearer picture of your baby's sleep patterns. You can then talk to your health visitor about any worries or concerns that you may have. The chart might consist of seven columns across for days of the week and 24 rows down for the hours. Colour in the hours that your baby is asleep during the day and night. You could also use the diary as a way of charting the times when your baby feeds, as sleep and feeding are closely related and a pattern may emerge which you and your health visitor could discuss together.

Where should my baby sleep?

Having your first baby can be a joyous, beautiful experience but it can also be downright terrifying. If you gave birth in hospital, you most likely spent your first night as a mother staring at your little bundle in awe and amazement, scarcely believing it really happened.

It's when you get back home that all the advice from well-meaning friends and relatives starts flying through your head. And the first thing that tends to leap to mind is: 'Are the baby's sleeping arrangements suitable?'

The Foundation for the Study of Infant Deaths advises that your baby sleeps in your room for the first six months of her life. According to research, the sound of you breathing can help your baby to 'remember' to breathe herself, and therefore reduce the risk of cot death (or SIDS, see pages 48–53).

Keeping her with you also has the considerable benefit of not having to get out of bed and virtually sleepwalk into another room for the two-hourly night feeds in the first couple of weeks. If you are buying a new cot before your baby arrives, you may want to consider a three-sided type in which the height of the mattress is adjustable, enabling you to sleep directly next to your baby, and literally roll over and feed without having to lift out your little one.

Newborn sleeping arrangements

In the first months, you may find a Moses basket the most convenient sleeping place for your baby as this will take up less space in your bedroom and be snugger for her. Newborns find confined spaces extremely comforting. If they can't feel anything around them, they get upset. And the more you can do to avoid upsetting a small baby, the better. Bear in mind that most babies will have outgrown a Moses basket by about four or five months.

Newborn babies spend double the time that adults do in REM sleep (see page 14), sleeping in much shorter cycles and hence waking up more regularly. Having very small stomachs, they also get hungry quickly. This means that, although she will sleep a lot at first, your baby will probably wake frequently to feed or be in need of comforting when she's not feeding. If you're lucky, your baby will sleep for longer at night, but in reality most babies cannot tell the difference between night and day for at least the first few months, and this will mean disturbed nights for a while.

It will take time to get used to your new baby. From your point of view as a new mother, apart from the physical effects of having gone through pregnancy and childbirth, it is likely you will have some emotional readjustments to make. Feeling the acute weight of responsibility for your new baby can be an emotionally overwhelming experience in the days following childbirth, and it will take time to settle into a routine. In addition, you may be dealing with conflicting emotions at this time that may affect your interactions with the people around you.

For example, you may experience feelings of inadequacy, anxiety or helplessness when confronted with what can seem at first the insurmountable feat of motherhood. This is normal in the beginning and as you grow more confident in your own skills as a parent, these worries will usually pass. If such feelings linger, however, making it difficult for you to carry out simple tasks, you should consult your GP to rule out the possibility of postnatal depression.

Bedding

Newborns need to sleep flat on their backs, with no pillow. Some babies hardly move all night. Some don't stop – legs and arms flailing, head going from side to side. If you've got a non-wriggler, she will probably be fine with just a blanket. If it's a hot night, one layer is usually enough. Don't forget that a folded blanket is equal to two blankets, and that two blankets will trap heat in the middle. Overheating is a concern. Your baby will wake up crying if she's too cold, but getting too hot is also a concern as it can heighten the risk of cot death. Before you become too alarmed and start sleeping with all the windows open even when it's freezing, remember that babies in hot countries survive perfectly well. It's just a case of being sensible with the number of layers you put on your baby.

Also, remember to keep your baby's feet near the end of the basket or cot so she can't wriggle down under the blankets.

In the summer, a nappy, vest and one blanket will usually be enough for most babies in the UK, unless the weather is particularly unseasonal. Think about how hot you get and remember that your baby is a person, just like you; just a really, really little (and squawky) one.

For the **gurgle** video on **Swaddling your newborn**, go to **gurgle.com** and click on **Videos**

Mum's top tip

When I had my first baby, I felt really exhausted and anxious. I battled on because I thought all new mums felt the way I did. It was only when I talked a bit more to my midwife that she recommended I go to see my GP, to make sure my baby blues didn't become anything more serious. My heartfelt advice is to talk with your carers about all your worries – a trouble shared...

Baby sleeping bags

If you've got a little kicker then a baby sleeping bag might be best. This is essentially a sleeping bag that your baby wears like a garment, leaving her arms free while her body and legs remain covered, no matter how wriggly she is.

When your baby gets a bit older, she will be able to undo the zips and poppers herself (handy hint: turn the sleeping bag back to front so that the zip is out of reach), but when she's tiny, a sleeping bag can be a fantastic way of keeping her comfortable in her cot. They come in different tog ratings for summer and winter, and are washable, so are easy to pop in the washing machine and tumble drier when the inevitable accident happens.

Because your baby will become very used to her sleeping bag, it's a good idea to take it with you when you go on holiday so that bedtime feels familiar, however different the surroundings are. (For more about sleeping arrangements on holiday, see pages 174–7.)

Moving to a cot

At some point, your baby is either going to grow out of the Moses basket or you're going to want a quieter night. Now's the time to think about moving your little one into a cot. If she's used to having daytime naps in one, it won't be a completely new experience.

Make sure your baby monitor is working and that you know how to use it. (You may be wondering why your child is so quiet only to discover you've left the monitor on the 'talk' setting!) For the first few nights, you'll probably be more awake than ever as you listen to every tiny rustle and sigh magnified a hundred times through the monitor, and then eventually you'll turn the volume down a notch or two. For your baby's first night in a cot, keep the routine exactly the same as before: bath, story, milk and bed.

Reclaiming your sleep

One of the most important items of soft furnishing in your baby's room is blackout fabric. Get a blackout blind and then curtains to go in front of it. Babies aren't completely in tune with adult sleeping patterns; they rely on Mother Nature to wake them up and, as far as they're concerned, wake-up time is when they can see daylight. During the summer that can be as mind-blowingly early as 4.30am!

When you were doing night feeds you were probably quite familiar with that sort of time. Now, though, it's time to reclaim those Zs! You want your baby to stay asleep until you decide it's getting-up time. While she's unlikely to humour your 10am lie-in on a Sunday, 7.30am is undoubtedly preferable to 5am.

Mum's top tip

I had a Moses basket for my first baby, a petite girl. She was in it for six months and it was great for carrying her in from room to room. However, when I had my boy, he was only in it for four months as he soon became too big. I needed to transfer him to a cot, so for the first few nights I put him in the Moses basket inside the cot until he got used to being in the cot, which must have seemed huge in comparison to the Moses basket.

New mothers = no sleep

According to a recent survey, new mothers survive on an average of three and a half hours' sleep a night (not that you needed an expert to tell you that!) and their sleep doesn't return to normal until their babies reach the age of 18 months.

The study, carried out by *Mother & Baby* magazine, involved a poll of 3,000 parents and suggested that gadgets and monitors installed in the home of almost every new parent are to blame. Apparently the installation of two-way monitors, breathing alarm equipment and, in some homes, video monitors to watch the child while he sleeps means that most mothers wake up at the slightest noise from their baby.

The study also revealed that although most mothers thought that advice from their parents or grandparents was outdated, they could in fact learn something from it, even if they didn't follow it to the letter. As Elena Dalrymple, editor of *Mother & Baby*, explains: 'Half of grandparents believed that a baby should cry himself to sleep. While leaving a tiny baby to cry himself to sleep is definitely not recommended nowadays, a mum should still aim to put baby to bed awake and let him settle himself to sleep.'

Fathers came under fire in the poll, as research showed that many were getting a full night's sleep in the early months. More than half the fathers said they 'hardly ever' got up during the night (55%) and that their average night's sleep was more than seven hours in the first four months. Fewer than a quarter (23%) ever woke up when their babies cried at night!

The survey found that almost half of mothers had been told by their parents to leave their babies to cry in order to get more sleep. On the other hand, a third had also been told to give up breastfeeding, despite all the medical advice to continue for six months or more. Three-quarters had two-way alarms, one-fifth had breathing sensors and one-eighth video monitors. The survey also found that, in their desperation to get their babies to fall asleep, two-thirds of parents had cot mobiles, half had musical nightlights and one-third rocking cradles. One in ten parents downloaded music that replicates the sound of being in the womb to help their baby fall asleep.

Thanks to *The Times* and *Mother & Baby* magazine

Seven hours sleep = a long life

The secret to a perfect night's sleep has been revealed as having exactly seven hours, no more, no less.

Researchers from the University of Warwick and University College London have found that those who get less than seven hours a night have an increased risk of mortality and are twice as likely to die from heart problems. But those who get more than seven hours' sleep at night may also be also putting their health in jeopardy and face an increased risk of dying from non-cardiovascular diseases.

Francesco Cappuccio, from the University of Warwick, states that lack of sleep could be linked to an increase risk of weight gain, high blood pressure and type 2 diabetes. According to Cappuccio: 'Fewer hours' sleep and greater levels of sleep disturbance have become widespread in industrialized societies. Sleep represents the daily process of physiological restitution and recovery and lack of sleep has far-reaching effects.' He adds that the link between too much sleep and poor health, while indicated by the study, is still unclear and in need of further investigation.

Currently one-third of the UK adult population regularly sleeps for five hours or fewer a night. The average night's sleep is seven hours. Previous studies have shown that women are more likely to suffer high blood pressure than men as a result of too little sleep.

Thanks to the *Daily Express*

Mum's top tip

Here's my recipe for a good sleep routine: at three weeks, I started to get my little boy into a routine, putting him down to sleep at about 10pm, then doing the next two feeds with dimmed lights in his room, keeping it as dark as possible throughout the night. At first he slept for around 5–6 hours but he's now sleeping 12 hours solid every night.

Sleep deprivation

Sleep deprivation is an inevitable consequence of having a new baby. According to a recent BBC survey, new parents lose a staggering two months of sleep in the first year of their baby's life. They can expect to lose up to 90 minutes' sleep each night, which can tot up to a whole night's sleep every week.

Add to this the fact that women claim to lose more sleep than their partners do (1% of women said they could sleep through their baby's cries compared with 43% of men), and you can see why sleep deprivation can put a strain on relationships. This is why it is important that you have lots of support from your partner. Talk to him before your baby is born about how to share out some of the sleep disruptions when your baby arrives, and you won't feel so alone.

Of course, you may be one of those lucky people who can survive on small amounts of sleep, but, coupled with the demands of your new baby, most people will find they get less rest at night than they need. For this reason, plan your time well. Don't worry about the housework when your baby is small, use nap times as an opportunity to put your feet up and even have a little doze yourself. You need to conserve your energy, not expend it, at this stage.

The good news is that usually, by about three months, babies begin to settle into much more of a routine and sleeping should be more predictable for everyone concerned. Here are **gurgle's** top tips for dealing with sleep deprivation:

top tips

- Nap when your baby does, or, if this doesn't seem to work, ask somebody to babysit for an hour or two while you sleep.

- Don't feel guilty: in some parts of the world, the new mother's mother takes over for the first 40 days!

top tips

- Exercise (see overleaf): even if it is just a spin around the block with the pushchair, getting some fresh air and upping your heart rate a bit is essential for helping your body rest properly later.

- Avoid bringing unnecessary stress or pressure into your life. Make sure you are able to say no to people who might not realize how tiring your new role is. This includes demands from bosses, partners, friends or family. Make yourself a priority at this time.

Boosting your energy levels

It may seem counter-intuitive to exert yourself when you've just had a baby and your energy levels are low, but gentle exercise can help boost your flagging spirits as well as bring other health benefits.

After having your baby you can start thinking about becoming physically active again whenever you feel ready, although most women find fitting in a fitness regime a struggle. It is advisable to wait until you have had your six-week check and the go-ahead from your GP. If you have had a Caesarean section, it will be eight weeks at least before you will be able to start a normal exercise routine, maybe more if you had an emergency section.

Exercise will help to get your body back into shape, reduce the possibility of postnatal depression and increase your energy levels. After you have given birth, your midwife should supply you with an exercise information sheet for you to follow. This will include simple exercises for improving circulation and for strengthening your pelvic floor to ensure continence.

The general consensus is that ten minutes of exercise a day, such as a a short walk, will help you to build your fitness levels. After your six-week postnatal check-up, you may increase this activity. In any case, at first you should not attempt to get straight back to exercising at the level you may have been pre-pregnancy. Avoid abdominal work and be careful not to lift heavy objects as this may strain your back. When stooping to pick up your baby, make sure you bend your legs and keep your back straight. Exercising in water, walking and gentle postnatal yoga are the best ways to build up your fitness again. High-impact exercise should be avoided because your body will be more susceptible to injury at this time. If you are breastfeeding then you should feed before exercising and make sure you have adequate support from a good bra.

For the **gurgle** video on **Postnatal exercise**, go to **gurgle.com** and click on **Videos**

Sharing the load

Becoming a dad

Male partners will also be experiencing their own new set of emotions about the changes that have taken place. It can be hard for them to empathize with what their partners are feeling; for some men it may be difficult to understand why their partners have suddenly become weepy or anxious. Communication is of course the key. Try to talk to your partner and tell him what you are experiencing so that he is able to support you properly.

A lack of sleep (and of adult company!), not to mention a never-ending mountain of domestic tasks to complete, often means new parents go past each other like ships in the night. The baby becomes the main focus of the relationship and other things fall by the way. The good news is that this is a temporary state of affairs and, with a little work, it can be changed. After an initial period of adjustment, you will start to feel like a proper couple again and not just parents attending to your baby's every need.

Support from your partner

One of the most common complaints from new mothers is that they feel unsupported by their partners. This may be to do with the fact that often it is the father who returns to work first, leaving the mother to deal with what feels like around-the-clock baby care. Try to make sure you make time for each other. Considering that, in many countries a new mother has the support of another female relative for the first month at least, it is hardly surprising that in the UK, where women are expected to get on with it (often alone), new mums often feel a little isolated as they try to adjust to life with a new baby.

BBC News recently reported the findings of a *Mother & Baby* poll (see pages 26–9) which demonstrated that half of all fathers 'hardly ever' or 'never' get up in the night to tend to their crying babies. In addition, 'six out of ten of the mothers said they resented their male partner for not getting up when the baby cried in the night'. If this is the case within your relationship, it's best to address the issue, as lack of sleep can cause great resentment if one partner is always getting more.

Make sure you have lots of support from your partner, relatives or friends and don't be afraid to accept people's offers of help. Grab sleep in snatches and don't overdo things. This is an emotionally and physically demanding time for you and you shouldn't underestimate its effects on your mind and body. Look after yourself! Finally, remember that although at times it is tough, this stage won't last for ever and there will come a day when you are misty-eyed and nostalgic about this sleep-deprived time. Honestly!

Supporting each other

If your partner is working during the week, then perhaps you could negotiate at least one night a week where you are given the opportunity to sleep all the way through, uninterrupted. A crying baby in the wee small hours can be difficult to deal with alone and team work ought to be the order of the day. If you don't address important issues like this, strain on the relationship will become apparent. Try to discuss the ways in which your partner can support you and those that aren't practical for him. Sometimes, just having the emotional support of someone around you is very important. If you have a shoulder to cry on, you will be able to meet the day-to-day challenges with much greater ease and confidence, so make sure you talk through all this with your partner so that he knows what you need from him.

Mum's top tip

Don't think you have to be supermum! Let your partner know how much you need him and love him. Let him learn how to look after your baby at the same time as you're learning. One of the nicest things I remember from when our baby was little was him having a bath with Daddy. Great Daddy–baby bonding, while Mummy had some well-earned 'time out'!

Strengthening the bond with your partner

Although having a baby is a very exciting time, it can also be a difficult one. Suddenly, you and your partner are making the transition from being a couple to becoming a family. Although you both have so much to look forward to together, you won't be able to enjoy the quality time with each other that you're used to.

Spontaneous weekend breaks and those long weekend lie-ins are all a thing of the past now. The sacrifice will have been worth it, but it does take some getting used to. Like it or not, having a baby puts quite a strain on your relationship and while many partnerships will flourish, some buckle under the pressure.

Communication is the key if you want your relationship to survive your new addition. Once your baby is asleep (finally!), set some time aside to talk to your partner about this new phase in your lives. Express your emotions and explain how you feel. Make sure that you build on your existing partnership and work together, not against each other. Enough of your energy will be spent looking after your baby without wasting more on petty bickering.

Don't sweat the small stuff

Research has shown that the strongest relationships are those in which the male partner has a deep respect and admiration for his partner and her new role as a mother. He mustn't belittle her in any way; she may have given up work to be a full-time mum, and he should appreciate this and not feel jealous or hard done by.

If you and your partner do snap at each other, don't beat yourself up about it. Parenting is no mean feat and you're bound to feel tired at the end of the day. Don't underestimate the impact having a baby will have on your lives: it will alter everything but, if you let it, it will change your life for the better.

Most new parents suffer from sleep deprivation in the first few months and this is enough to make anyone ratty. If you are feeling irritable, you're most likely to take it out on the person closest to you – your partner. It's perfectly normal for this to happen. Just remind each other why it is happening and make an effort to apologize and spend some time together the following evening.

Sharing tasks and making time for each other

Share tasks with your partner. Even if one of you is working, you should both take responsibility for your child. Alternate what you do; for example, one of you could change your baby's nappy one evening while the other gives her a bath. Then switch around the following day. This will help prevent either of you feeling that you are being taken advantage of.

Although you won't feel like leaving your baby at first, you need to make time for yourselves. It's normal to go off sex when you've recently given birth, as suddenly you don't seem to have either the time or the inclination to be sensual and physical. However, it's

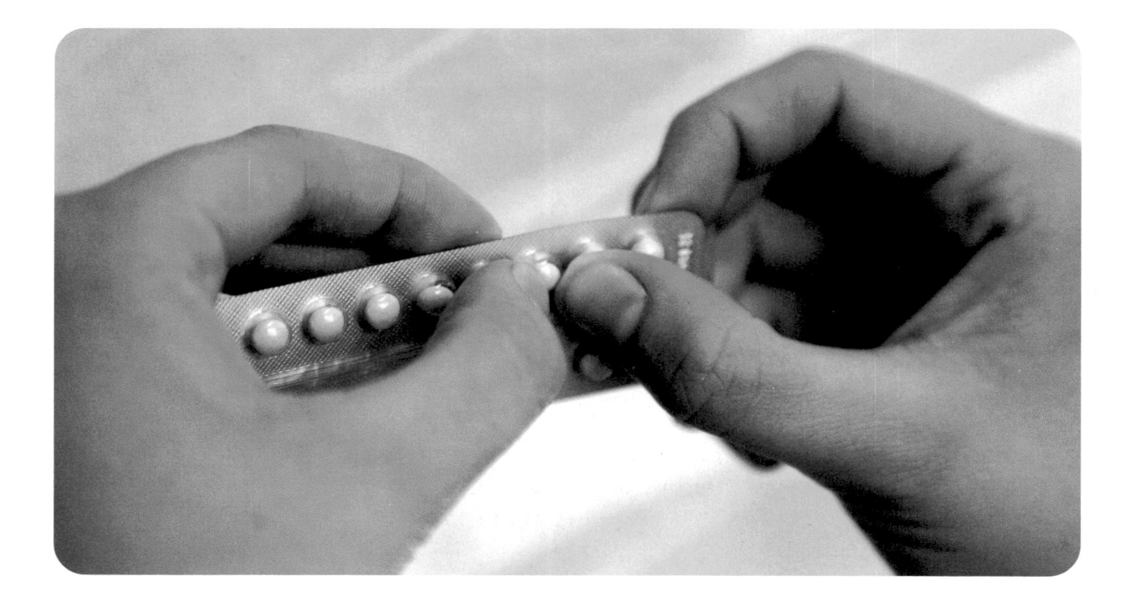

important to remember that intimacy is a vital part of any relationship as it helps to make you feel closer to your partner. This isn't to say that you should rush things. It's probably best to wait a few weeks after you've given birth before you resume having sex, as your body needs time to recover. Wait until your GP has given you the all-clear.

You and your partner need to make time for each other; newborn babies can destroy any shred of romance, so be aware that this is an area you'll have to work on together. Try to get a babysitter now and then (see overleaf); if you're always listening out for your baby, you're not giving yourself a proper chance to relax and unwind.

Why not enjoy a special meal together, with some classic aphrodisiacs on the menu such as oysters or chocolate (or both!)? Light some candles and put on some of your favourite music to really set the scene, and see where the night takes you... Remember to use contraception, though, as it might not be your intention to fall pregnant straight away!

Mum's top tip

I found that, after the birth of our son, it took some time before I felt ready to make love again. So my partner and I would massage each other with wonderful, scented oils. It's a very intimate, loving way to spend time together and you will appreciate your tired neck and back muscles getting some special attention!

When can I start using a babysitter?

When you choose to leave your child with someone else is up to you. Some women take months before they are able to leave their babies, whereas others start to plan their first night out straight away.

Leaving your baby with someone else also depends on whether you breast- or bottlefeed. If you breastfeed, unless you express your milk for the babysitter to give to your baby, you will only have a short window of time before he needs to be fed, and before your breasts need emptying again.

If you do plan to go out, choose your babysitter carefully. Ideally you want to use either your partner, your parents or siblings, or close friends who have had children of their own. Using an inexperienced teenage babysitter, or someone who hasn't looked after newborn babies before, is not a good idea. Try going out for a short amount of time at first so that you and the babysitter can get used to it. Remember to leave your contact information and details of where you are going with your sitter, together with details of what to do in an emergency should one arise. Make sure you're able to get back to your house quickly in case your sitter is having a tough time.

Who should babysit?

Many teenagers make a bit of money through babysitting, and while you may be happy for a friend's daughter or neighbouring youngster to babysit for you, you should consider whether a teenager has the necessary maturity and presence of mind to look after young children or babies, particularly if something should go wrong.

There is no minimum legal age for babysitters in the UK, although RoSPA and the NSPCC strongly recommend against allowing anyone under the age of 16 to babysit young children. While many teenagers place babysitting advertisements at local schools or in the local paper, it's best, when employing a young babysitter, to go by personal recommendation from friends or family.

Be sure to interview any prospective babysitter carefully, and try to ascertain how she or he would cope in certain situations. For example, ask what she would do if your baby wakes with a fever during the evening while you are out, or starts vomiting. You might want to suggest, if she hasn't already and is going to be babysitting for you regularly, that she take an introductory first-aider's course. Find out what experience she has of looking after young children – and be sure to check all references thoroughly.

Preparing your babysitter

If you have found someone you like, you might want to invite her over to your house to spend some time with your baby before her first evening's babysitting. This will give you a good opportunity to see how she interacts with your child, the kind of activities that she might do with him and – most importantly – how well your baby responds to her!

Use this opportunity to show your sitter round the house and explain where things are kept, such as first-aid supplies. Go through your child's routine with your sitter so that she is familiar with what you expect from her. This will lessen the disruption and hopefully help things to go smoothly. If she is looking after a young baby, be sure that she is aware of when to give feeds and where the nappy-changing kit is, and give her tips on how best to comfort your baby if he becomes distressed.

It's important to set house rules for your sitter, about bringing friends over, watching television or using the phone or internet. Make sure that you leave emergency contact telephone numbers – preferably both a mobile and a landline number, if possible – for your sitter, and tell her where you will be and when you anticipate getting back.

If you are going to be later than anticipated, make sure that you let your sitter know. Leave some refreshments for her – soft drinks and something with which to make a light snack should be enough, but discuss this with your sitter beforehand. Lastly, ensure that your sitter is able to get home safely. If you are returning late, either offer to give her a lift home or pay for a taxi.

Cost

Rates for babysitters may vary enormously depending on the age of the sitter, the ages of the children, location and hours. Get a feel from other parents in your area who employ babysitters, or from your prospective sitter's referees.

Mum's top tip

Be prepared to feel rather odd the first time you go out without your baby. When my husband and I went out for the first time, our baby was around six weeks old. I felt I had forgotten how to be a couple and I kept thinking I had left something behind, which I had – my baby! The strange feelings soon passed and you'll be fine too, as long as you've left your baby with someone you really trust.

Helping twins sleep at the same time

Two of them to deal with! The thought of getting one baby down to sleep and into a routine is daunting enough, let alone two babies and at the same time. However, don't panic: it is a perfectly achievable goal and the general consensus from parents with twins is that it is possible.

Caring for twins is obviously going to be hard work, and you will have hugely conflicting emotions about the whole process. Once your babies have arrived, though, and they are not just an unthinkable dream, you will soon start to plan how to make life with twins work for everyone.

Mum's top tip

My twin boys used to sleep in the same cot – they seemed to be more relaxed and to sleep better if they were close to each other. I was amazed to find that one twin waking or crying did not seem to disturb the other twin. As they grew, we put them in separate cots, but next to each other. They still share a bedroom and sleep all the better for it.

You need to have a good support network in place, especially if your partner is out working. It can be lonely at times dealing with a new baby, and with two to look after, you will have double the workload. Don't be afraid to ask for help from your family and friends. Also, joining an organization aimed at parents of twins or multiples can help you to meet other parents in a similar situation. Sometimes there will be a twins group in your local area that you can visit.

A good bedtime routine

Establishing a good bedtime routine (see pages 62–5) is crucial, no matter how many babies you have, indeed, if anything, it is even more important than with a single baby. Your twins need to learn when it is time to wind down and sleep. So try to create the right kind of environment to help make this happen. In the early days, it is also possible to put them to sleep together. Having spent nine months sharing a rather cosy little space means your babies will most likely enjoy being close to each other outside the womb.

In terms of adapting generally, try not to put pressure on yourself to maintain your household, work or social life to the standard that you did before having your babies. You are allowed to make a slow return back to the world. You have a different reality now to contend with and feeling bad about not doing the vacuuming or missing a friend's birthday, when you are up to your ears in nappies and breastfeeding, is pointless. These things will get easier; for now, just give yourself a break. Try to get a little time out for yourself each week, even if it's only for an hour or two. Keep the lines of communication open between yourself and your partner (see pages 38–41), and regularly discuss how you are feeling to prevent possible resentment over your domestic workload.

Reducing the risk of SIDS (sudden infant death syndrome)

Sudden infant death syndrome (SIDS) – commonly known as 'cot death' – is the sudden, unexpected death of a seemingly healthy infant. Although most parents are plagued with worry that something will happen to their child in the night, the chances of your baby succumbing to SIDS is very small – about 1 in every 2,000 in the UK, which is roughly 300 babies a year. This figure may seem frightening, but because parents have been taking steps to avoid SIDS there has been a 71% decrease in the UK of SIDS deaths since 1991.

Why does SIDS happen?

There is no single known cause of SIDS. Current areas of research are looking into the respiratory system and temperature control mechanism of young babies, which are very immature at this stage and may make it harder for infants to rouse themselves if, for example, the bedcovers go over their heads.

There are certain factors that appear to make the risk higher. Babies whose mothers smoked during pregnancy and postnatally have an increased risk of SIDS, in addition to those born to mothers who received poor antenatal care. Mothers under the age of 20 also have a higher risk of their babies succumbing to SIDS, but this may be more to do with smoking and/or poor antenatal care. Premature and low-weight babies are also at a slightly higher risk of SIDS. For reasons unknown to doctors, cot death is slightly more common in boys and less common in Asian babies. Babies with a sibling who died due to SIDS are also slightly more at risk.

The environmental factors that increase the risk of SIDS are babies overheating, sleeping on their tummies, sleeping with toys or pillows in their cot, or sleeping on soft or loose bedding. In addition, if your baby is exposed to tobacco smoke, she is at a greater risk of SIDS.

Does the risk go away?

SIDS is most common in babies between the ages of two weeks and a year, the peak age being between two and four months. In rare cases, cot death can occur between 12 and 24 months.

What can I do to reduce the risk?

The good news is there are lots of ways you can help to reduce the risk of cot death.

- Always put your newborn baby to sleep on her back, never on her front. Make sure anyone who is looking after her is instructed to do this too. Once your baby is six–nine months old, the risk of SIDS is considerably reduced and although you should still place your baby to sleep on her back, you shouldn't be overly concerned if she moves into another position while she is asleep.

- Use a firm mattress (if you have borrowed a cot from somebody, always buy a new mattress for your baby) and tightly fitting sheets. Remove all your baby's toys, any pillows, loose bedding, sheepskins and cot bumpers from the cot.

- Don't let your baby overheat. Don't dress her too warmly or put a hat on her head. The ideal room temperature is between 16 and 20°C (61 and 68°F), so it is a good idea to keep a thermometer in the room to check on temperature changes. Don't overload your baby with blankets and sheets; use our guide for what bedding to use (see overleaf), or use a special baby sleeping bag, which can control your baby's temperature and stop her from slipping under the covers.

top tips

- Place your baby with her feet at the foot of the cot when you are putting her to sleep so that she cannot slip down underneath the covers. Tuck her sheet or blanket in at the sides so it cannot move around too much.

- Keep your baby's cot in your room for the first six months.

- Never put a hot-water bottle or an electric blanket on your baby in her cot.

- Never smoke or let anyone smoke in the same house as your baby. Even going to a different room to smoke does little to reduce the exposure to the toxins in cigarette smoke.

- Keep your baby's face and head uncovered at all times when inside the house.

- Don't add more covers to your baby's cot if she is unwell and has a temperature. Instead swap her blanket for a sheet and remove some of her bedclothes so she doesn't get too hot. (For more on keeping your baby cool, see pages 92–3.)

top tips

Room temperature and bedclothes

How many blankets your baby needs depends on the temperature of the room she is sleeping in. Below is a useful guide to follow:

Room temperature	Number of blankets
15°C (60°F)	A sheet and four blankets
18°C (65°F)	A sheet and three blankets
21°C (70°F)	A sheet and two blankets
24°C (75°F)	A sheet and one blanket
27°C (80°F)	A sheet only

A cellular baby blanket, with tiny holes in it so that air can circulate around your baby, is ideal. Most baby shops sell these.

For the **gurgle** video on **Keeping your baby cool in hot weather**, go to **gurgle.com** and click on **Videos**

If you sleep in the same bed as your baby

- Make sure your baby is flat on her back and nowhere near your duvet and pillows, which may cover her head.

- Put a lightweight cotton baby blanket over her rather than using your duvet or quilt.

- Don't share a bed with your baby if you or your partner have recently drunk alcohol, smoked, taken medication or drugs, or are very tired. (For more on co-sleeping, see pages 90–91.)

Can a dummy help prevent SIDS?

In helping to reduce the risk of SIDS, there has been research into the possible benefits of using a dummy when you put your baby down for a sleep. Experts are still unsure of why a dummy might help, but they don't recommend using one before four weeks for a breastfed baby in case she then rejects her mother's nipples. With a bottlefed baby it is fine to use a dummy before four weeks. (For more on dummies, see pages 86–9 and 150–55.)

Trying not to worry too much

Many parents are overly preoccupied with the fear of SIDS, which can be more harmful than good. They fear, for instance, that immunizations could increase the risk, whereas there is nothing to indicate that this is the case. Try not to worry unduly. Resist the urge to check your child's breathing every two minutes, which will disturb and disrupt her sleep patterns. It's perfectly normal to feel paranoid and to check your baby occasionally, but try not to let anxiety take over. Some parents invest in a monitor that alerts you if your baby suddenly stops breathing, but they often cause more worry than good if they are faulty or if you check them constantly. If you are concerned about SIDS, talk to your GP or health visitor about your worries. It may be worth learning infant resuscitation to increase your confidence that you will be able to to deal with an emergency in the unlikely event that one should arise.

For the **gurgle** video on **Reducing the risk of Sudden Infant Death Syndrome**, go to **gurgle.com** and click on **Videos**

Happy bedtimes: birth to six months

Your guide to sleep routines: birth to ten weeks

Getting your child into a routine is the bane of most new parents' lives and tends to dominate new-mum discussions. There is no right or wrong when it comes to establishing a routine, but it is useful to introduce a structure into your baby's day so that he knows what is coming next and so that you can start to feel less disorganized and more in control.

Babies love routines and they're good for parents too. It's great to know that you'll be having a bit of 'you' time between 7 and 11pm, for example. If you try to do the same thing each night – bathtime, story, pyjamas, cuddle and bed – your baby will start to know what comes next and bedtime won't be a complete shock.

gurgle expert Sue Whytock, a nursery nurse for many years, maternity nurse and recently presenter of programmes such as *Help! I'm a Teenage Mum* and *Britain's Youngest Mums and Dads*, recommends that you start a routine when your baby is about three weeks old, as it's important to spend the first few weeks bonding with him. She has provided **gurgle** with some tried and tested routines for parents to follow. The first (see overleaf) is a routine suitable from three to ten weeks, while the second (see page 97) is from three to six months.

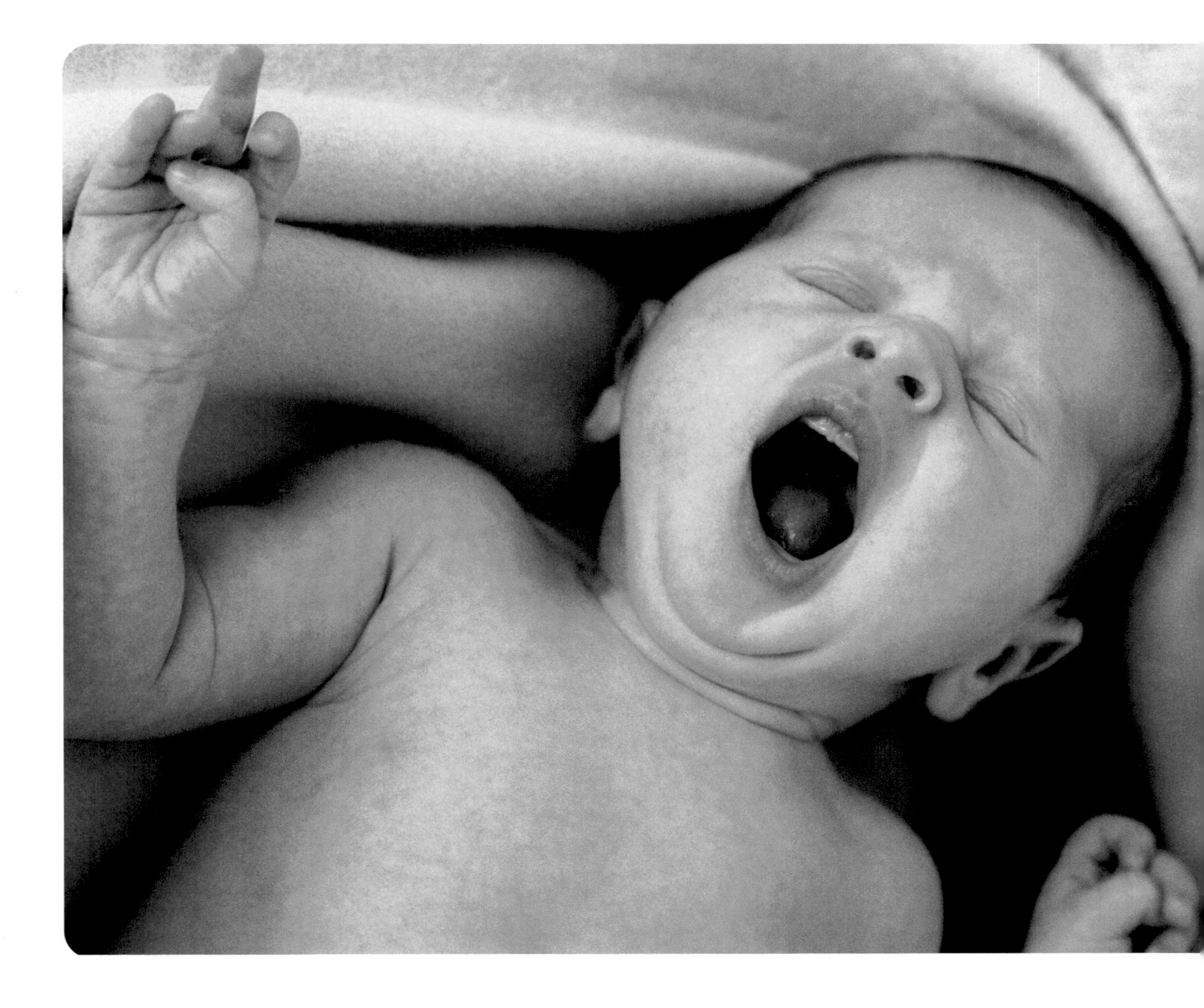

The trick is to follow the routine but to stay reasonably flexible. It shouldn't take over your life or stop you leaving the house. In essence, it is to be taken with a pinch of salt! You will probably make your own adaptations to the routine laid out below, but it makes a good starting point.

Typical daily routine

7am Wash and change ready for food, then feed.

8am Playtime on mat.

8.30am Sleep back in cot or Moses basket.

10am Another feed.

11am Playtime or out for a walk.

1pm Feed.

2.30pm Sleep in cot or Moses basket.

3.45pm Wake up ready for feed.

4.00pm Feed. Some babies will sleep after this feed and others will lose this nap and stay awake till their next feed.

5.45–6pm Bathtime.

6.30–6.45pm Feed, then bed. Feed your baby in the room he's going to sleep in. Keep it semi-dark and quiet and settle him down for the night after his feed. When you leave the room, turn the night light off.

10.30–11.00pm Feed. Change your baby's nappy to wake him up so that he feeds well before going back to sleep.

3.00am Feed. Don't change the nappy unless you have to as this will wake your baby up completely and you want to keep him drowsy so he falls back to sleep.

Settling your premature baby

If your baby is premature then you will need to be patient and expect your nights to be disturbed. Her stomach is absolutely tiny and she will need to feed little and often in the early days. The fact of the matter is, you cannot expect to start any kind of routine with a baby who has made an early arrival, as she needs to feed and sleep as much as she can in order to catch up and stay in good health.

What can I do to help?

Premature babies, those born earlier than 37 weeks, need lots of love and support, and it is very important for you and your partner to remain close to and touch your baby. Lots of hospitals now advocate 'kangaroo' care for premature infants, where you and your partner are encouraged to carry your naked baby around inside your clothes and against your skin. Ask your special care baby unit (SCBU) for details. Talking to and stroking your baby so that she can feel you close and hear the voices she heard while inside the womb are going to help her get stronger, and will help to establish a bond. Your SCBU will assist with breastfeeding, which is important for premature babies, both nutritionally and to help them gain weight, as well as to strengthen the bond between mother and child.

Swaddling your baby (see pages 74–7) may help to mimic the close comfort of the womb and she will probably sleep better if she is wrapped in this way. The reality is that she will need to sleep for most of the time, but will wake often to feed. As she grows older you can start to think about establishing a routine, but for now you must go with what she wants and needs.

Having a baby earlier than planned can be an enormous shock, and caring for your newborn in the first few months will probably be very different from how you imagined, especially if she is admitted to a neonatal unit. The good news is that you can still do many of the things you originally planned – including breastfeeding – even if your baby has been born very early.

Breast milk is great for your baby, offering her protection against germs through your own antibodies. It is also easier for babies to tolerate than formula milk and provides all the nutrients and nourishment they need to grow and develop. A mother's milk is especially valuable to premature babies because their immune systems are weaker. It can boost their defences against illness while they're catching up developmentally in those vital first few months.

If your baby has been born very early, she may not be ready to feed directly from your breast straight away and might have to be fed through a drip to start with, particularly if there are breathing difficulties. From there she can progress to breast milk, which is likely to be fed to her via a tiny tube that will go through her nose and into her stomach. With supervision from the nurses, it may be possible for you to help with tube-feeding your baby. This can help you bond with your baby as well as enable you to see how much she is benefiting from your milk.

Establishing a bedtime routine

The way to improve the chances of your baby sleeping well through the night is to ensure you establish a good bedtime routine for him as early as possible. Babies, like all children, need to know their boundaries; this helps them to feel secure. Your baby will benefit from having a (reasonably) fixed schedule of events at bedtime, as this will teach him to relax and wind down so that he's ready to sleep.

You should start the process of settling your baby down for the night by choosing a similar time each evening. For example, at six o'clock you could run a bath for him. Bathing your infant on a daily basis will relax him and prepare him for bed. It is also an opportunity to bond with him and spend some one-on-one time together. Ensure that the rooms you will be using are warm enough for when he is taken out of the water.

After a bath, wrap him up in a soft, warm towel and lay him, facing upwards, on a changing mat or your bed. Dry him carefully and put on a fresh nappy. You could use this period to give your baby a massage or a cuddle. Next, put on his sleep clothes and check he has the right amount of bedding (see page 52). Make sure he is neither too hot nor too cold as either could make it more difficult for him to fall asleep straight away.

Dim the lights slightly and check your baby won't be disturbed by too much noise from anywhere in the house. All things in moderation, though; it can be a real hindrance if your baby needs complete silence to get to sleep, especially during the daytime, and some mothers swear by a healthy dose of background noise so their baby will learn to sleep without being too disturbed by chatting or music.

Now you can give your baby his last feed of the evening. Often babies will fall asleep when they have this feed, but in order not to build up too much of an association between the two things, it might be an idea to try and put him down in his cot prior to him actually falling asleep. Otherwise he could wake up and cry for the missing comfort of breast or bottle. Experiment a little to see if this is what happens. He may not wake up again, so just establish what works for you.

Don't leave a little baby in an adult bed. At this stage, a cot or crib is the best place for sleeping. And make sure your baby sleeps on his back, with his blankets tucked in around him; instances of cot death (or SIDS, see pages 48–53) have been linked to babies being placed on their stomach to sleep, even though this was the advice given to new mothers in the not-so-distant past.

Try to be flexible about the routine so that you don't restrict your own life unnecessarily. If you plan on going out from time to time, try to accept that the bedtime ritual can't always take place in the same way. Your baby will not suffer, and you will certainly benefit, if you both have a little 'time out' from each other.

Mum's top tip

I would recommend you try to get your baby into a bedtime routine of bath, feed, bed at a time that suits you. That way you'll at least have some sort of evening to yourself! It will be hard at first, especially if your baby has become used to going to sleep later in the evening, but it should start to fall into place within a few weeks if you persist. Babies like structure and routine as it makes them feel secure, so if you can do it, it could be a great help to you both; it definitely was to me.

Typical bedtime routine

1 Pick a time to start winding down before bed. Make sure the room your baby is going to sleep in is warm and not overly light.

2 Run a bath and spend some time washing your baby (the warm water will help to soothe him) before taking him out.

3 Wrap him up in a soft towel and lay him on a changing mat or bed in the room he will be sleeping in. Dry him thoroughly and put on a fresh nappy.

4 Massage or cuddle your baby before you dress him for bed. Don't forget to talk to him and tell him what you are doing. Even young babies like to hear their parents talking to them. They might not understand the words, but they will understand the tone and be comforted by your voice.

5 Feed your baby his last feed before bedtime (don't forget to wind him).

6 Finally, put him down to sleep, so that he is lying on his back, in his crib or cot.

Bathing your baby

Babies usually enjoy bathtime, and it can be a good way of getting them used to being in and around the water from an early age. By the same token, even one bad bathtime experience can put some children off baths and water for a long time.

The most important thing about bathing your baby is that she feels secure while in the bath. It's a foreign environment for her and she will be a little apprehensive, so make sure that she feels happy and safe. A small baby won't need a full bath every day, and you can simply 'top and tail' her, using a bowl of warm water, baby lotion and a soft cloth or flannel to wash her top half and nappy area. Avoid using soap (even baby soap) or wipes until she is at least six weeks old. Try and give her a full bath every couple of days.

Bathing equipment

You don't need much in the way of equipment for bathing a newborn baby. The important thing to remember is never to leave your baby unattended in the bath, not even for a moment. Even if you use plastic bath seats or other forms of support to hold your baby in place, you must never leave her alone as she could wriggle out of position and slip under the water.

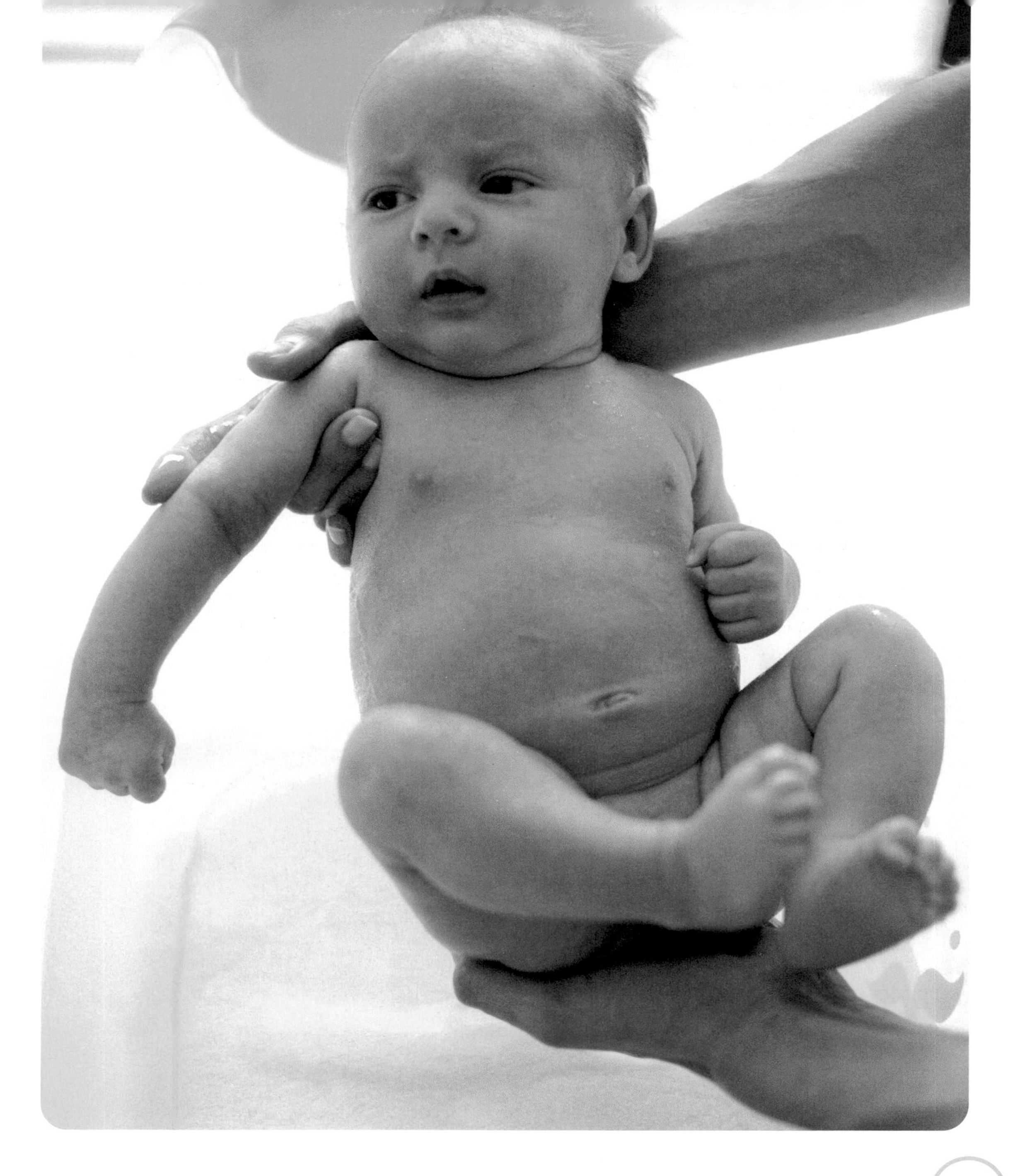

Some bathtime basics

1 BABY BATH

For small babies up to four or five months, a specially designed plastic baby bath is ideal. Some baby baths fit neatly over the sides of the main bath and can be filled from the taps and drained away directly into the main bath.

2 BATH SEATS

The big advantage of a bath seat is that you have both hands free to wash your baby. Seats generally come in two different forms – for small, non-sitting babies and for babies who can sit. The former are generally moulded seats on which your baby can sit reclined, supported under his arms and between his legs, the latter simply a round seat with arm rests. Both should have suckers that attach firmly to the base of the bath to prevent slipping. Always check that the seat you are buying will fit into your bath, as some can be very wide. And never leave your baby unattended.

3 OTHER BATH SUPPORTS

While some mums feel confident enough to hold their babies in the bath using no additional means of support, various bath supports are available. These include floats, nests and sponges, all of which will support your newborn safely in the bath. Which type you buy depends on you and your baby. Support sponges are about the size of your baby; you immerse them in the bath and lay your baby on top so that his head and neck are out of the water. Some supports are ideal for smaller babies: the TummyTub, for instance, consists of a narrow plastic tub that holds your baby upright while you bath him.

4 BATH THERMOMETERS

Many mums find it hard to get the temperature of their baby's bath absolutely right with the traditional 'elbow test', so it's a good idea to invest in a bath thermometer.

5 BABY BATH AND SHAMPOO

Unless your baby's hair is particularly abundant, you can wash it using just warm water for the first few months. As it becomes thicker, you may want to use a little baby soap or a mild baby shampoo.

6 BATH TOYS

Toys can help make bathtime fun, as long as they are safe. Toys for the bath need to be clean and waterproof and preferably made from plastic so that they don't disintegrate over time. Bubble bath can be fun for older babies, but do check in case it irritates their skin.

Bath safety

The bath can be dangerous for small babies and young children. No child should be left unattended in the bath, even for a very short period of time. Keep the water shallow (no more than 10–13cm/ 4–5in) and use a plastic non-slip mat to prevent your baby from slipping. Some taps can get very hot and remain so long after the bath is run, so be sure to cover these with a flannel or towel.

HOLDING YOUR BABY IN THE BATH

For a newborn baby, you will need to support his head and shoulders with one hand, placing your fingers under his armpit. When taking him out of the bath, make sure that you have a towel already laid out nearby, and hold him very carefully, as wet babies can be very slippery.

Mum's top tip

I found that bathing my baby in the kitchen sink when he was newborn worked a treat. The sink is at a good height – you don't have to bend over the bath, giving yourself backache – and the whole experience is more enjoyable. Mind you, my son grew fast and was soon too big for a kitchen-sink bath – more's the pity!

Sleep and breastfeeding

Depending on the way you approach sleep for your breastfed baby, there is really no reason why you should not get a good night-time routine going. Something that is sometimes frowned upon is breastfeeding your baby until she falls asleep. The reason for this is that your baby should be able to sleep without 'sleep associations' or 'cues' like your breast.

If you feed your baby to sleep every night, you may be storing trouble for yourself as every night she will expect to be breastfed to sleep. She will not be able to sleep without the comfort of your breast, which could mean you are the only person able to soothe her when she wakes in the early hours.

Feeding your baby to sleep every night could also mean that she's merely suckling on the breast and not really taking in enough milk to keep her satisfied. Some people suggest that your baby should be fully awake when you feed her. If your baby is particularly sleepy while feeding and keeps drifting off, it might be worth breaking the pattern by changing her nappy or walking round the room with her, so that she's then sufficiently awake to finish her feed and doesn't wake up two hours later hungry for more!

Some mothers disagree that feeding their babies to sleep every night is a bad thing, and are happy to start a feeding precedent and establish this routine. This is a matter of personal preference. Indeed, if, for example, you are co-sleeping with your baby (see pages 90–91), breastfeeding can actually be a wonderful bonding time that hardly disturbs your night anyway. At any rate, night feeding helps to maintain your milk production. Equally, if you need to cut out a feed, your body should adapt accordingly.

Alternatively, if your baby will take a bottle, your partner could give her the night-time feed with a bottle of expressed milk, thus ensuring you are not the only person leaping around after midnight and giving you the opportunity to catch up on some sleep. You will learn what works best for you and your baby.

Swaddling your newborn

Swaddling newborn babies has been a tradition for thousands of years, across many different cultures, mainly because they love being cocooned in this way. Wrapping your newborn firmly in a soft blanket reminds him of being in the womb. He feels secure and sleeps more contentedly. While experts are divided on the benefits of swaddling, many people swear by it.

As adults, we like to pull our covers tightly over us and curl up into a ball for comfort, and some babies are the same. Research has suggested that swaddling can reduce the risk of cot death (or SIDS, see pages 48–53) in young babies, because it helps to keep them on their backs and stop them from slipping down underneath the bedcovers.

For sleep-deprived parents, swaddling may be the answer, because babies tend to sleep more deeply if they are swaddled. This is because swaddling stops them from waking themselves up due to the 'Moro' or 'startle' reflex, where they involuntarily jerk their legs and arms around. It can also stop them from scratching themselves with their fingernails, which grow rapidly in the first few months and are usually hard to cut. Because it applies gentle pressure on the abdominal area, swaddling is also thought to help to reduce the symptoms of colic (see pages 156–63). Ask your midwife or health visitor to show you how to swaddle your baby, or follow the instructions overleaf.

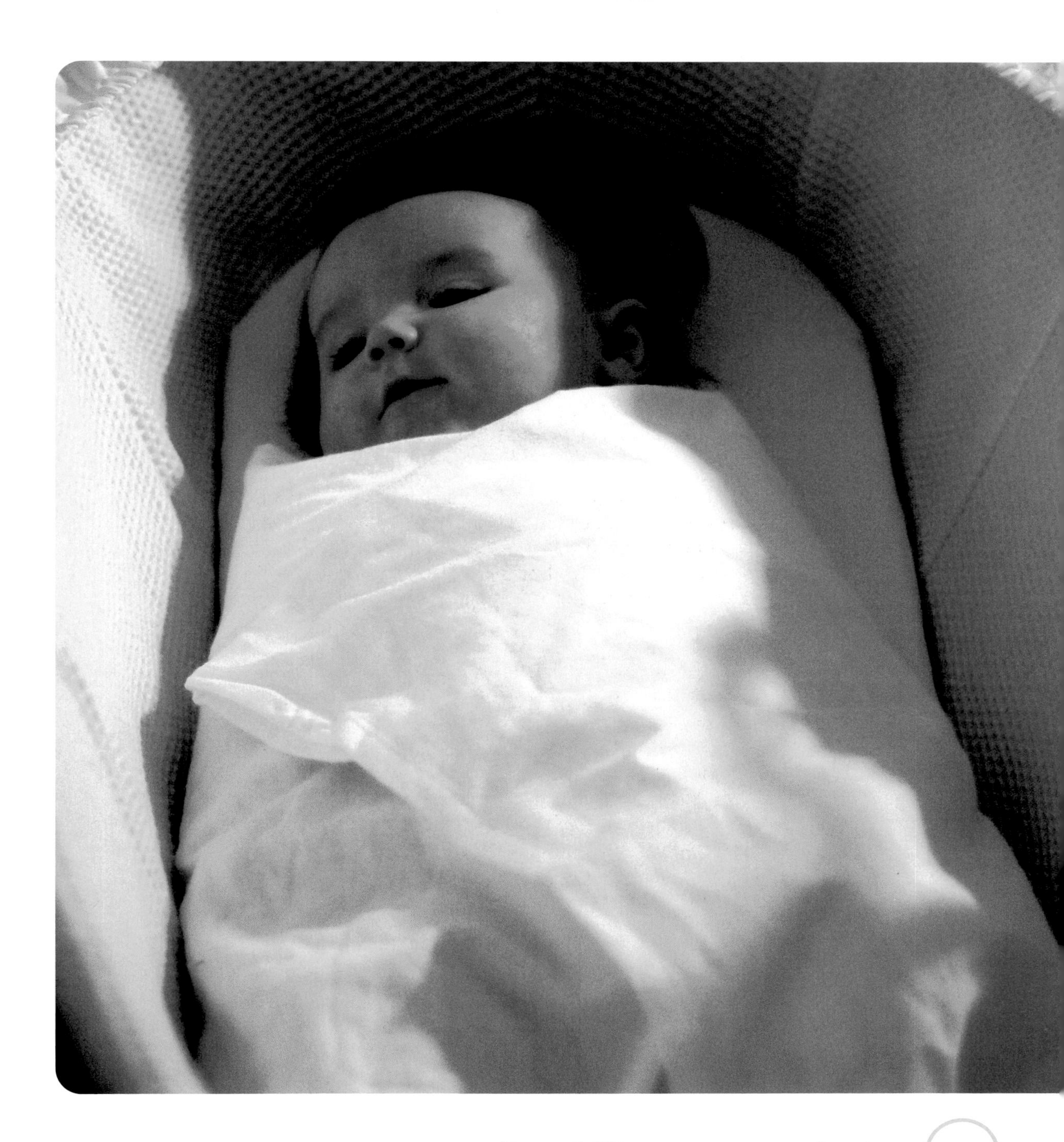

Some babies don't like feeling so restricted, however, so if after a few attempts your baby clearly doesn't take to being swaddled, you may need to find another way of settling him down. Try placing him in his cot or Moses basket with his feet at the foot of the cot, and laying a blanket over him. You can tuck the blanket in firmly at the sides and at the bottom, so that he is secure and he still cannot move around too much and wake himself up. As long as his feet are at the bottom of the cot, he cannot slide underneath the covers.

How to swaddle your newborn

Use a small cotton sheet, special swaddling blanket or a cellular blanket – with lots of tiny holes in it so that air can circulate around your baby's body. Don't use a synthetic blanket or anything too warm, such as a quilt. In addition, your baby's room shouldn't be too hot or too cold. Somewhere between 18 and 21°C (64 and 70°F) is best.

1 Place the sheet or blanket diagonally on a flat surface and fold the top corner down by about 15cm (6in). Place your baby in the middle of the sheet with his head on the fold.

2 Take the right corner of the sheet and wrap it tightly around your baby, tucking the leading edge underneath his left arm and back. Fold the bottom corner up and tuck it in.

3 Take the left corner of the sheet and wrap it around your baby, tucking it underneath him on the right side. Make sure you aren't wrapping him too tightly or covering his head.

Can my newborn sleep alone?

It is up to you where your newborn sleeps. Some parents want to co-sleep, taking their baby into bed with them (see pages 90–91), while others keep their baby's cot or Moses basket in their room. The government recommends that you keep your baby in a cot in your room for the first six months to keep an eye on him. This can also be easier for night feeds, of course.

Some newborn babies snuffle, sigh, hiccup, breathe heavily and generally make a lot of noise while they sleep, making it impossible for parents to share a room with them. If this is the case, move your baby into a cot in a room nearby and put a monitor by your bed so that you can hear when he needs you.

For the **gurgle** video on **Swaddling your newborn**, go to **gurgle.com** and click on **Videos**

Mum's top tip

I practised swaddling a large doll before my baby was born and as a result I felt more confident about swaddling my newborn baby when the time came. My advice is don't be afraid that your baby will feel restricted – they love the security, it's like being in the womb again. Some newborn babies startle themselves awake but if they're securely wrapped, their movement is gently restricted and they carrying on sleeping.

Checking on your baby's breathing at night

New parents often find themselves checking on their baby's breathing during the night. This is absolutely normal and nothing to be embarrassed about.

However, if you are constantly checking and worrying to the point that you cannot relax, you might need to speak to your GP, as being overanxious can make life very difficult for you at this demanding time. If you are worried about cot death (or SIDS, see pages 48–53), then you should consider creating a safe sleeping environment for your baby (see pages 50–52). This should help you worry less so that you no longer feel the need to check on your baby all the time.

What your baby's breathing should sound like

It can be hard even to hear a newborn breathing, as it is so light. Your baby's breathing is not constant, either, sometimes sounding quite fast and sometimes quite slow. She may even pause for a few seconds without breathing, which to the uninitiated ear can be quite alarming. These different breathing patterns are all absolutely normal and nothing to be concerned about. The slightly erratic style of breathing will change as your baby matures and her lungs grow stronger. Until then, her breathing may sound shallow.

What isn't normal breathing for a baby

Most breathing difficulties arise because your baby has developed some sort of infection. Because her respiratory system is immature, you should consult a doctor as any infection could be potentially serious. If your baby's breathing is laboured (she is having trouble taking breaths and you can see her ribs drawing quickly inwards), seek medical advice at once. This is because your baby has very small airways and it is important she is assessed immediately.

Mum's top tip

I found that having a baby monitor was a bit of a mixed blessing. When I was downstairs and my baby was sleeping upstairs, I would always have the monitor on. However, when the monitor was next to my bed, I found that I kept waking up every time she so much as snuffled or moved in her cot. So I stopped using it at night – as she was only in the next room, I could hear her when she cried but was no longer woken by every sound she made.

Why is my newborn baby crying?

It can seem as if your newborn is doing nothing but crying, morning, noon and night. This is because her only form of communication is to wail like a banshee. The good news is that there are a only a few reasons why newborns cry, and it will probably be one of these things that she needs.

IS SHE TIRED OR OVERSTIMULATED?

At the end of the day, usually between 5 and 6pm, babies can get grouchy, basically because they are trying to process everything that has happened that day. Your baby may be overstimulated and finding it hard to wind down, so try playing soothing music to her, talking gently and removing toys, mobiles and pictures books. If she is overstimulated, she may also find it hard to sleep (a bit like an adult going to bed after tackling some paperwork), so try to wind everything down before bedtime or a nap so she's relaxed and her mind is clear.

IS SHE HUNGRY?

Babies eat all the time because their tummies are small and get empty quickly, so it is not uncommon for them to feel hungry only an hour after they have last fed. While some babies can go three hours between feeds, many need feeding all the time in the form of frequent short 'snacks'. At this stage in your baby's life, it is best to indulge her. Don't think about implementing a strict feeding routine until she is over six weeks old. Most midwives recommend that you stick to feeding your baby every three hours, but this of course depends on your baby and you should be flexible.

CHECK HER NAPPY ISN'T WET OR SOILED

Babies feel uncomfortable in dirty nappies, and because they have tiny stomachs their bodies expel waste at a fast rate. Expect to get through about 10–12 nappies a day in the first few weeks, until your baby's tummy grows and matures enough to retain more food.

HAS SHE GOT WIND?

Babies often cry because wind gets trapped in their tummies as they gulp in air when feeding. After each feed, pat and rub your baby's back firmly, leaning her slightly forward so that any wind comes back out. She may bring up a tiny amount of milk, but this is normal. Lots of newborn babies suffer from what is referred to as colic in the first three months. This is slightly different to wind, as it usually makes babies cry excessively and does not go away easily, making it difficult to soothe your baby. A likely cause is windy stomach cramps, although no one really knows for sure. (For more on colic, see pages 156–63.)

For the **gurgle** video on **Soothing a crying baby**, go to **gurgle.com** and click on **Videos**

IS SHE TOO HOT OR TOO COLD?

Newborns cannot regulate their own temperature, so you need to be very aware of how hot or cold your baby might be. The room should be heated between 16 and 20°C (61 and 68°F), warm enough for a baby dressed in a vest and sleepsuit (see also pages 50–52). Newborns feel the cold if they are wet, so when you dress your baby after her bath make sure she stays covered up and warm. Depending on the season and weather, your baby may need a hat if you go outside, but always take it off when you come indoors, to stop her overheating. You can check your baby's temperature by feeling her tummy or the back of her neck. If she feels clammy, she is probably too warm.

IS SHE BORED OR UPSET?

Even newborns can get bored if they are lying in the same position for a long time with nothing new to look at. A change of scene might be all that is needed. Try picking her up and taking her into another room or going for a walk around the garden. Or she might be feeling a bit out of sorts and simply in need of a cuddle and to hear your soothing voice.

IS SHE IN PAIN?

Babies who are in pain tend to cry in a slightly different way from those who are hungry or bored. Painful cries are often shrill screams, followed by silence and short gasps. You will probably know instinctively if your baby is in pain, but if you are worried, see your GP or health visitor.

All babies are different and while some cry all the time, others seem more contented and settled. You can't spoil a newborn if you attend to her cries, and the more cuddles and reassurance you give your baby, the more you will help her to feel loved and secure.

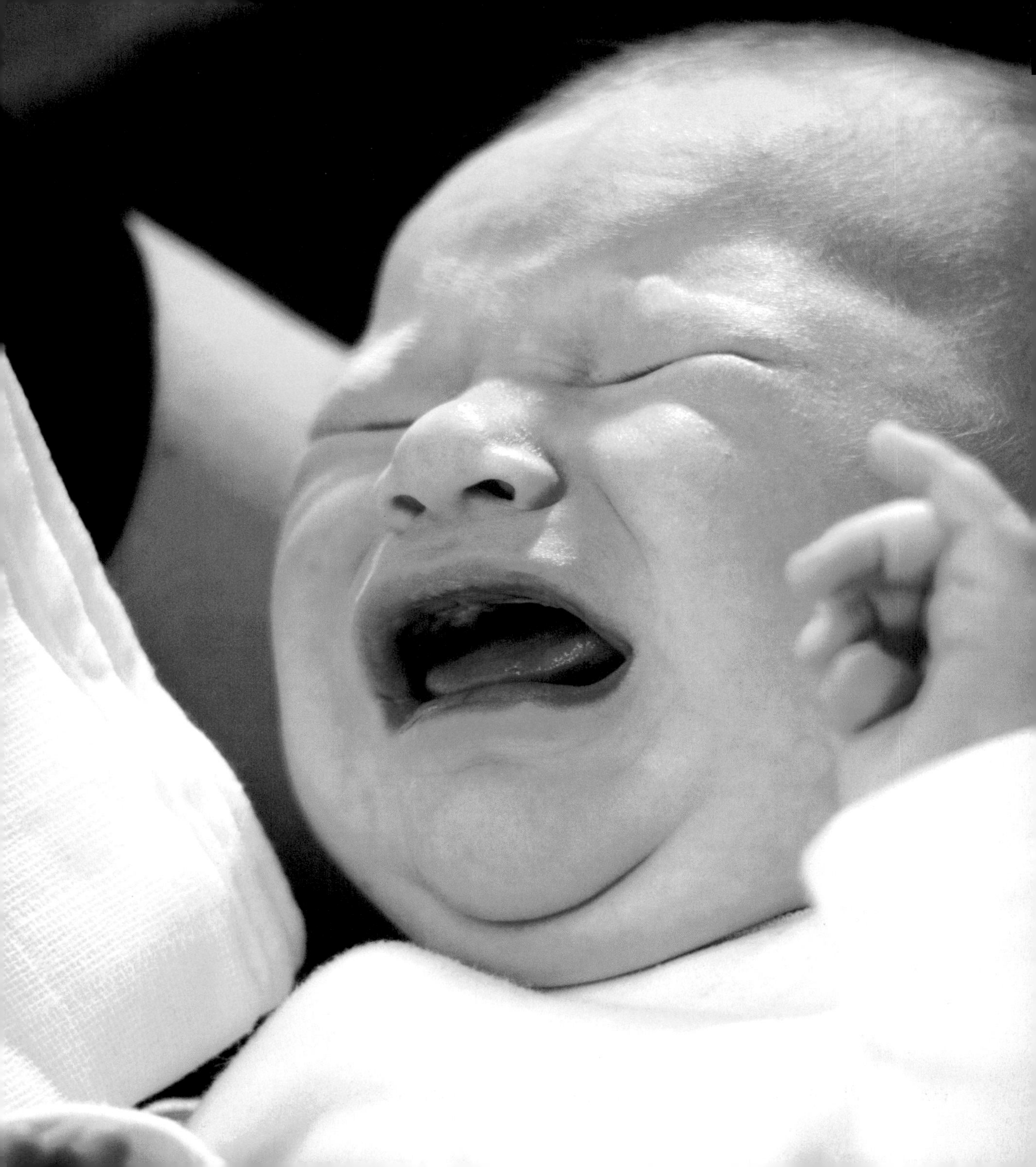

Soothing your crying baby

All babies cry, so don't be alarmed if your baby spends much of his time in tears. It can be somewhat over-whelming, though, so here are gurgle's top tips on how to deal with a crying baby.

There are lots of ways to soothe a crying newborn.

top tips

- Rock him backwards and forwards in your arms, on a rocking chair or in his pram.
- Sing soothing songs to him – he loves to hear your voice. Play nursery rhymes, classical music or your favourite radio station to calm him (and you) down.
- Carry him in the baby sling. He will feel warm, secure and close to you, and you can be hands-free for a while.
- Feed your baby – he could just be hungry.
- Give him a comfort object such as a dummy or a bit of cloth that smells of you. (An old T-shirt of yours may also do the trick.)
- Give your baby a warm bath. This can also help colicky babies relax and feel sleepy before bedtime.
- Stroke your baby rhythmically. Try massaging him with baby oil before bed, or stroking his temples very gently.

- If it all gets too much, put your baby down somewhere safe (in his cot or pram) and leave the room for a few minutes while you calm yourself down. Try not to be angry with your baby for crying. He is communicating to you in the only way he knows.

It's worth it because...

No matter how much your baby cries, he still only has eyes for you. It is amazing how quickly he will stop crying when comforted by Mum – just the smell of you as you enter the room can settle your baby. Research shows that even a four-day-old baby will stare at his mother's face longer than anyone else's. It will not be long before you see his first smile and those days and nights of pacing up and down your house with a crying baby will be a distant memory.

Mum's top tip

I would encourage you to rule out any physical reason for incessant crying. My son Max cried incessantly when he was around 3–4 weeks old. Turned out all the crying was not due to anything emotional but to reflux (see page 165). I made the mistake of thinking he was really hungry and was feeding him nearly every time he cried, whereas that was just adding to his problem and he was suckling on the bottle for comfort and not out of true hunger. He only ever settled when I held him a particular way, as that brought relief, but one dummy and over-the-counter medicine for reflux later, I have a different baby who feeds every four hours and is much more contented.

Can a dummy help my baby get to sleep?

Most newborn babies won't need a dummy, and will be comforted with a cuddle or a song, but some babies are more 'sucky' than others and may prefer the comfort of a dummy. You can give newborn babies dummies straight away if you wish, but try to go for an orthodontic type as these are supposed to be better for developing teeth and gums.

It is best to view the dummy as a short-term solution, however. You don't want your child to come to rely on the dummy, so use it sparingly, giving it only when other methods of comfort have failed.

Remember to sterilize the dummy after it has been dropped, and to keep a stock of clean dummies nearby. A dummy clip, attached to your baby's clothing, will stop it falling on the ground.

Some babies will suck on anything they can find, be it a thumb, toes or a toy. They are usually the ones who will most benefit from a dummy, whereas others will be pacified with a cuddle or rocking. Giving a dummy to a very young baby may not be successful, as some newborns dislike the sensation of a dummy in their mouth.

Dummies and breastfeeding

If your baby has not mastered breastfeeding yet, giving her a dummy or switching from the nipple, which is soft and pliable, to a dummy teat, which is hard and rigid, is just going to confuse her. She may even reject the breast in favour of the dummy. In addition, if you give your baby a dummy before she has properly finished on the breast, you might be depriving her of the fatty hind milk that comes at the end of the feed.

So if you plan to breastfeed, avoid giving your newborn a dummy until breastfeeding is established – probably somewhere around four weeks. If your baby is bottlefed, it is fine to give her a dummy straight away. But be careful, as a dummy can easily pacify your child, preventing you from finding out the underlying cause for her crying. Is she hungry and is the dummy just staving off the inevitable? Is she feeling insecure? Is she cutting a tooth? Is she finding it hard to get to sleep on her own?

Cleaning dummies

Until your baby is weaned onto solids, dummies should be sterilized in the same way that you sterilize bottles. After this, thorough cleaning with warm, soapy water is enough to ensure the dummy is safe to use. Inadequate cleaning of dummies can lead to ear infections, as bacteria can travel down a baby's very short Eustachian tubes (connecting the ears with the mouth and nose).

Weaning your child off her dummy

Dummies can interfere with the development of your child's teeth, especially if she is still using one once her adult teeth start to appear, usually around the age of five or six. Some parents find it very hard to wean their child off a dummy, and while they feel embarrassed walking around the shops with a dummy-sucking toddler in tow, they are loath to face the battles they imagine will ensue when the dummy is taken away.

As your baby grows, try to give a dummy only at bedtime, taking it out of her mouth when she falls asleep, or restrict dummy use to the home only. Try and encourage your child to have a small toy instead for comfort, and emphasize the fact that she is a 'big girl' now and that dummies are just for babies. Once your child starts to speak, she is likely to find her dummy a hindrance and will rely on it less as she tries to communicate more.

Thumb-sucking

Some babies find their thumbs in the first few days. This can be handy as it means your baby can soothe herself and you won't have to deal with a sudden fit of crying due to a dummy falling out in the middle of the night or another inopportune moment.

There is no need to sterilize your baby's thumb, of course, as it will be clean enough. The downside to thumb-sucking is that it can be harder to stop your baby from doing it. While a dummy can be taken away, a thumb is always there and the older a child gets the more damage a thumb can do to teeth. Although there isn't much you can do if your baby takes to thumb-sucking, most children grow out of the habit by the time they reach pre-school age. (For more on sleep comfort habits see pages 150–55.)

Mum's top tip

My daughter decided of her own free will to stop sucking a dummy when my neighbour's new baby boy arrived. She adored him at first sight but was most put out to see a little baby sucking a dummy and decided that she was a big girl now and would put her dummy in the bin. We were amazed, delighted and very proud of her!

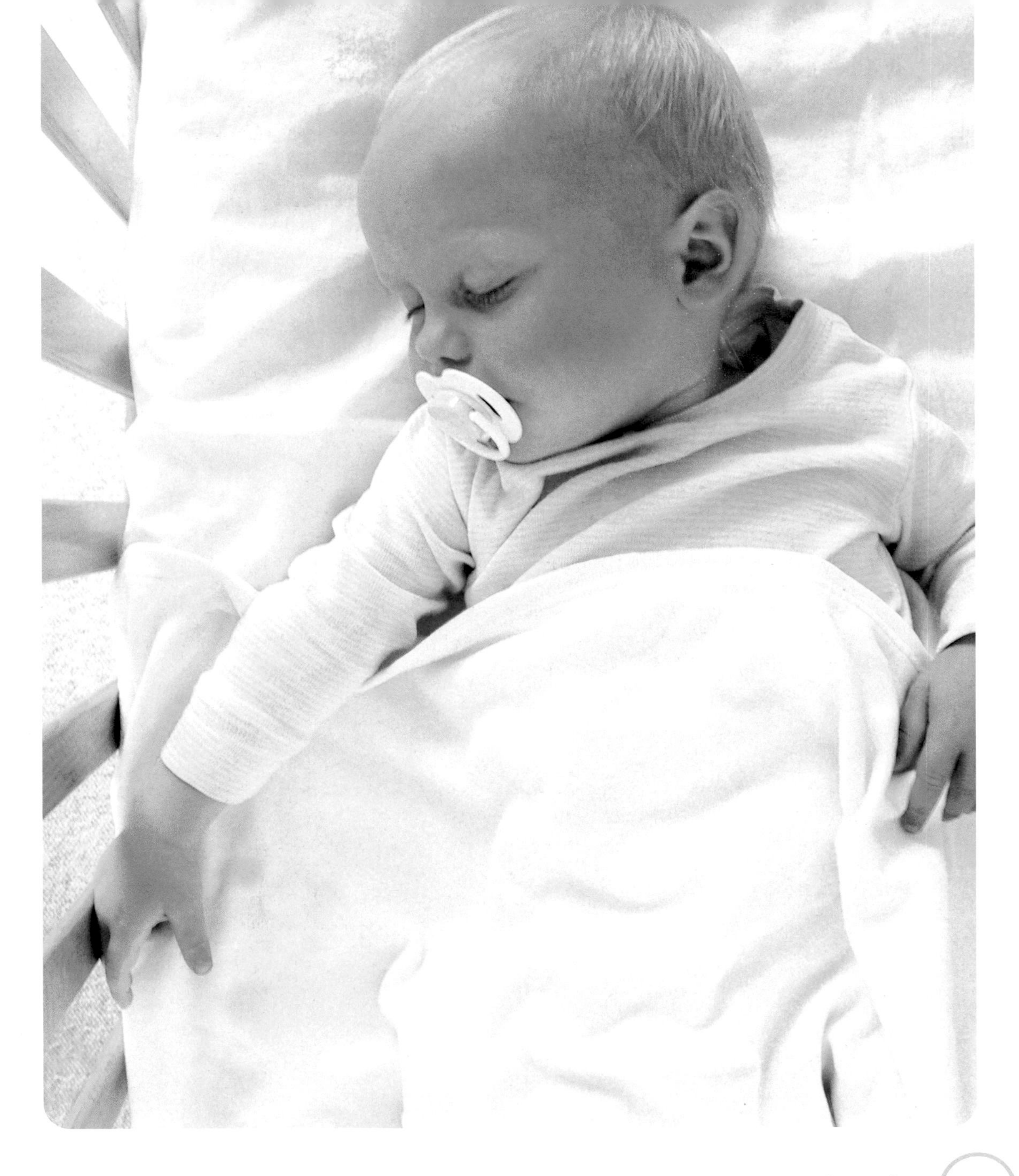

Should you co-sleep?

According to the Foundation for the Study of Infant Deaths (FSID), the safest place for your baby to sleep during the first six months is in a crib or cot in the same room as you. However, some parents choose to co-sleep with their baby. The term 'bed sharing' is used to describe a mother sharing a bed with her child to breastfeed or cuddle, but not for sleeping. Opinion is divided about the benefits or otherwise of co-sleeping.

Co-sleeping can be hugely beneficial, as different studies have shown. Everyone sleeps better and breastfeeding can be better established among co-sleeping babies and mothers. On the other hand, if certain risk factors are present – for example, if the parents are smokers or are under the influence of alcohol – then there is a greater risk of cot death or SIDS (see pages 48–53) or of the baby being smothered accidentally. Similarly, if either parent has a medical condition (insulin-dependent diabetes, for example), it is unwise to co-sleep in case of a temporary loss of consciousness occurring.

On the plus side, many people believe that co-sleeping helps your child to grow in confidence and feel secure, which will affect him positively as he gets older. It also allows you to bond with your child through physical closeness. Whatever the case, it appears that a great many parents do co-sleep, according to findings by the NHS, even if it wasn't planned prior to the baby's arrival. If you do choose to co-sleep, follow **gurgle's** top tips to ensure that your baby stays safe.

top tips

Top tips for safe co-sleeping

- Wait until your baby is three months old before co-sleeping. This is because he is at greatest risk of cot death (or SIDS, see pages 48–53) in the second month of his life.

- Don't sleep with your baby if he was premature (born earlier than 37 weeks).
- Don't co-sleep if your baby was less than 2.5kg (5½lb) at birth.
- Only sleep with your baby if neither you nor your partner smokes, has been drinking alcohol, or is on drugs or medication.
- If you (or your partner) are extremely tired, it is not wise to co-sleep.
- Use lightweight blankets rather than a heavy duvet and ensure that your baby's head does not become covered during the night.
- Don't leave your baby to sleep on his own in your bed.
- Make sure your baby can't roll out of bed and land on the floor, or become caught between the wall and the bed, as he might injure himself.
- Specially designed little mattresses are now available, with sides for keeping your baby in place on the bed so that you can all lie together without worrying you'll roll onto him. It might be a good idea to use one of these at first to get you used to co-sleeping.

top tips

For the **gurgle** video on **Safe co-sleeping**, go to **gurgle.com** and click on **Videos**

Keeping your sleeping baby cool in hot weather

It is important to make sure your baby does not get overheated when the weather is hot. As you yourself will know from experience, being too hot at night makes it difficult to sleep. Waking up with a dry mouth and a headache in a badly-ventilated room is unpleasant for anyone, whatever their age.

On a more serious note, extremes of temperature have been linked to cot death (or SIDS, see pages 48–53). To make sure your baby stays comfortable, you should check that the room she is sleeping in is about 18°C (64°F) in temperature.

Ensure there is no possibility of her head becoming covered up by her bedclothes. The way to do this is to put her in the 'feet to foot' position. Her feet should be touching the end of the cot. Some parents prefer their baby to sleep in a specially-designed baby sleeping bag with arms and a zip, thus preventing anything from covering her mouth or nose. This may be too warm when the weather is hot, however.

Don't place your baby's sleeping cot or Moses basket near a radiator (if it's on) as this could cause her to overheat rapidly. If the room is stuffy, some ventilation is advisable. Obviously, this does not mean an Arctic wind, but some fresh air is good as long as the room temperature can be maintained and your baby is not in a draught. Make sure, too, that she has been offered as much cooled, boiled water as she needs. Keep a baby thermometer in your baby's room so you can see if the temperature rises or falls.

If it is really hot outside, your baby will only need to sleep in a nappy and with a cotton sheet over her. Make sure the whole house or flat is well ventilated and ensure windows are open to allow a breeze to circulate. It is not a good idea to aim a fan at your baby as this will make her too cold, but you could put it on in her room for a while before she settles down for the night. You could also leave some bowls of water in the room to keep the air moist.

For the **gurgle** video on **Keeping your baby cool in hot weather**, go to **gurgle.com** and click on **Videos**

Mum's top tip

My first was a winter baby and I wrapped him up well. My second was born last June and I dressed her in only a vest some days and wrapped her loosely in a light sheet at night. My advice would be to buy some short-sleeved and sleeveless bodysuits because the weather and temperature can change from one day to the next.

Your baby at three months

By month three, you will probably be feeling like a seasoned pro and your baby will be starting to get stronger and more independent.

As his hand-eye coordination improves, he will suddenly discover his fingers and touch just about everything within reach. This is how he explores the world around him, so if you're wondering why he repeatedly touches things, it's just his visual and cognitive skills working together as he gets to grip (in more senses than one!) with his new environment.

If last month saw the first smile, this month will see lots more; he'll be gurgling and cooing at everyone. He'll reserve the special smiles for Mum and Dad, however – his two favourite people.

HIS HANDS

By three months, he might try batting at objects in front of him – again, evidence that his hand-eye coordination is improving all the time. Hanging brightly-coloured toys from his play gym or from the handle of his infant carrier on car journeys will encourage him to bat and grab even more. He will probably be able to grasp a rattle at this stage, but will be far more obsessed with his hands, which he'll stare at intently, pleased with his new discovery.

WHAT HIS WORLD SOUNDS LIKE

By the end of the third month, your baby's hearing will be improving all the time. He will be startled by a loud sound and wakened by loud noises or talking. This doesn't mean you should creep around the house when he is napping; it is good for him to have a bit of background noise. What's more, the womb wouldn't have exactly been peaceful, with stomach gurgling and outside sounds filling his ears. You may notice

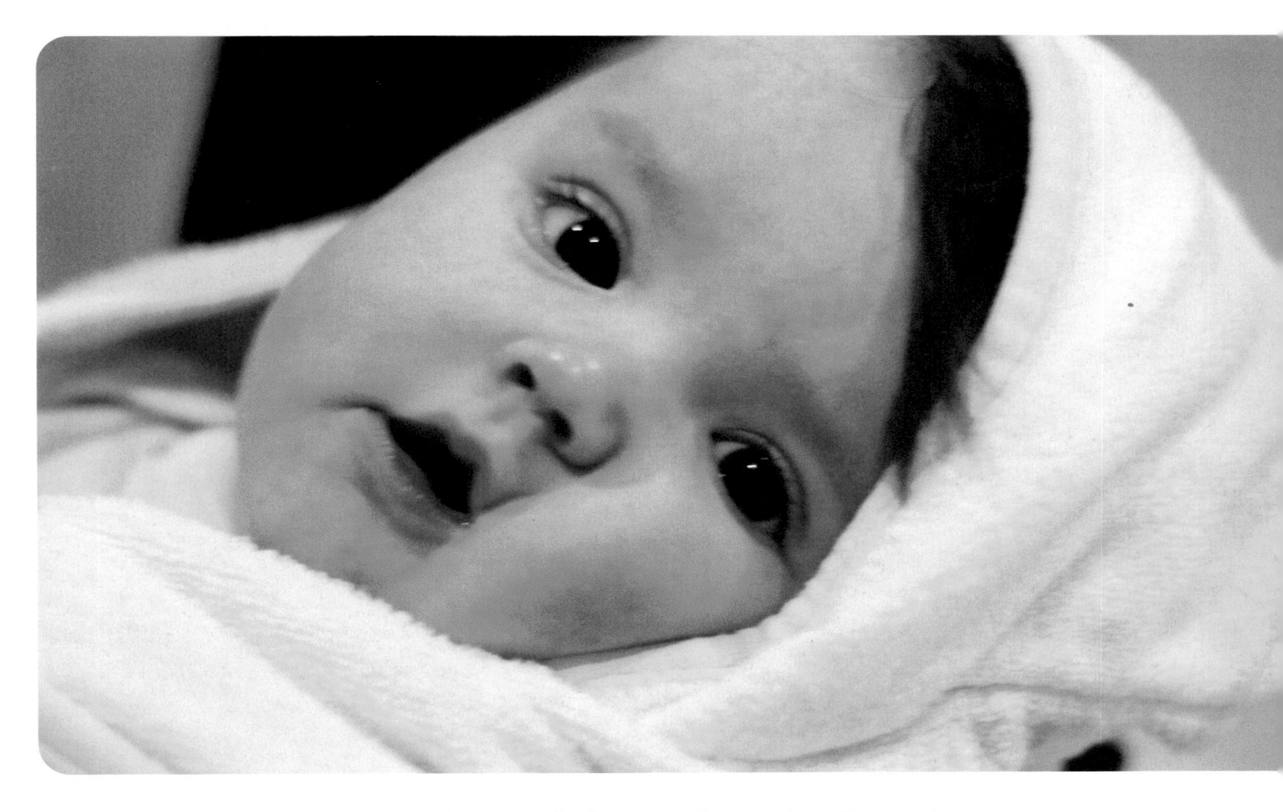

that he is soothed by the sound of your voice, and smiles and gets excited when he is spoken too (especially if it's you). Try to speak to your baby as often as you can, no matter how silly you feel. He'll be taking it all in.

ROLLING OVER

Some time between the second and third month, your baby may learn to roll over (some babies take much longer to do it and some don't at all). He will start by practising tiny baby press-ups when on his front and will graduate to rocking back and forth, side to side and eventually kicking and flailing his arms out like a little swimmer. One day he will flip right over! As this can happen at any time, it is important that you keep a hand on him when changing his nappy on a changing table or other high surface. Similarly, beds and sofas are not safe to leave him on unattended in case he attempts a roll.

Your guide to sleep routines: three to six months

By three months, it is probably time to start helping your baby get into some kind of routine if she is not already in one. Many parents obsess about this, mostly because of 'helpful' advice from others insisting that they should have a routine in place by now.

It may be worth taking on board some of this advice, however. For example, you were probably advised by your midwife to feed your baby on a three-hourly basis until she is old enough, her stomach being more fully developed, to drop certain feeds. If your baby has been feeding sporadically up until now, it might be a good idea to try the three- or four-hourly routine, just to give a bit of structure to your day. Babies actually love routines and yours might be happier eating at designated times rather than snacking throughout the day.

Three-month-old babies need about 14 hours of sleep, which roughly equates to four hours in the day and ten hours at night (see page 17). These aren't continuous hours of sleep as your baby may nap in two- to three-hour stretches or in a series of smaller naps throughout the day and night. No baby, toddler, child, teenager or indeed adult is the same when it comes to sleep, so resist the urge to compare your baby's sleep patterns with anyone else's. This is also a very rough estimate as some babies need very little sleep while others are fond of a long slumber. If you are worried about your baby's sleep patterns, consult your health visitor or GP for advice.

Typical daily routine

7am Wash and change ready for first feed of the day. Feed.

8.45–9am Sleep.

10.00–10.45am Wake up from nap.

11.00am Feed.

12.45pm Sleep in cot.

2.45pm Wake up and change nappy.

3.00pm Feed and playtime.

5.45–6pm Bathtime.

6.30–6.45pm Feed. Always give a little more at this feed (although if you are breastfeeding, this may be difficult). Feed in the room where your baby is sleeping and keep it semi-dark and quiet so that she settles for the night. When she is settled, leave the room and turn off any nightlights. If you can encourage your baby to fall asleep on her own (without being rocked or cuddled or fed to sleep), it will be better for you as once your baby learns to do this she will put herself back to sleep at night. For young babies, this will take some time.

11pm Feed. Change the nappy to wake your baby up so she feeds well. Keep the room semi-dark and quiet so she goes straight back to sleep after her feed.

4.00–4.30am Feed. After about three and a half months, you can start thinking about encouraging your baby to sleep through the night.

Top tips for happy bedtimes

- Keep your baby's room dark at night so she remains sleepy and doesn't wake up completely. You want to encourage her to sleep after you have fed and winded her, so try to make eye contact minimal, keep the room dark and avoid playing any games with her.

- Don't forget to wind your baby after each feed! Small babies have even smaller stomachs. This means that they may need feeding more regularly, as often as every two hours when they are very small. This should settle down once your baby grows a bit bigger and is able to take in a bigger feed.

- Playing lullabies or classical music can help to relax your baby and settle her to sleep at night. If she is sleeping in your room, it can help to relax you too!

- Read to your baby and show her the pictures. Even if she doesn't understand the words, she will love to hear the sound of your voice. Getting into the habit of reading will also help your baby to recognize words that are repeated and will eventually help with speech and understanding. In short, it is never too early to read to your child.

Story time

Even though your baby is tiny and can only respond to you with smiles or cries, now is the perfect time to start reading to him. It may seem strange to read aloud to a little person who does not respond, but you'll never have such a captive audience. Once your baby gets bigger, he will wriggle and squirm through story time, or want to pull the book apart, or get distracted by something else. With a small baby, you know you have his absolute attention.

Starting to read to your baby when he is small helps in a number of ways. Each time your baby sees, hears or feels anything, his brain processes the information and makes the connection between the pictures and the words he hears you saying. Eventually understanding comes and the pictures tie in with the words. Focusing on pictures also helps him to develop his eye muscles and, if the book has flaps or textured images he can feel, hand-eye coordination. Story time also creates a quiet atmosphere and a bit of bedtime bonding between you and your baby.

- If you are not a confident reader, read the book yourself a couple of times first to get some practice.
- Try to talk about everything you see before turning the page.
- Point at pictures and give the names for everything.

- Use a different voice for each character if you can. Even a high and a low voice helps your baby distinguish between characters and teaches him the different pitches and intonation used in language.
- Don't rush through the book; take your time and let your baby point at what he can see. Pointing is a skill a slightly older baby will master.

Bring back the bedtime story

According to child psychologist Dr Pat Spungin: 'The benefits of bedtime reading from an early age are evident, with 38% of children going on to read for themselves before bed. This is a healthy routine to get into as it will improve their creativity and reading and writing skills, as well as helping them to relax and sleep better.'

Mum's top tip

My babies all loved having a story read to them last thing at night. The more often they heard the story, the greater their enjoyment seemed to be. There is nothing more special than that lovely moment when you settle your clean, fed baby into his cot and reach for the bedtime story. It's a very special time and passes all too quickly, so enjoy every moment!

Night feeding and when to phase it out

It's a question that many a sleep-deprived new mum often asks – 'When will my baby sleep through the night?' Of course, we've all heard stories of those marvellously considerate babies who sleep through from ten until six in the morning from the word go, but the reality is that most small babies simply aren't able to go for long stretches at night without a feed.

However, by the age of six months your baby should have a more established sleeping pattern and should be able to sleep through from 11 or 12 at night until five or six in the morning. Many parents see a big improvement in their babies' sleeping patterns once they are on solid food. They tend to feel fuller and so don't wake so often during the night for a feed.

So why is your baby still waking in the night to feed? The chances are she isn't really hungry but there is some other factor at play.

SHE CAN'T SETTLE HERSELF BACK TO SLEEP
Many babies who find it hard to settle themselves back to sleep have got into the habit of nodding off while having that last breastfeed at night. You can help your baby to break the habit by not letting her fall asleep on the breast when you put her down, but playing some gentle music instead after her last feed

or reading her a story. The more she gets used to going off to sleep without Mummy, the easier it will be for her to do so when she wakes in the night.

SHE'S GOT INTO THE HABIT OF WAKING AT THAT TIME

Even grown-ups find that sometimes they go through a phase of waking at the same time every night. If your baby has been waking routinely for feeds at the same times, it may well have become a habit which you need to try and gently break. If you are sure that she isn't really hungry, try and get your baby used to settling herself back to sleep instead of having a breastfeed.

SHE'S TEETHING

Teething babies tend to wake more frequently in the night simply due to the discomfort they are experiencing. A little infant ibuprofen or paracetamol should help to take the edge off the pain and make it easier for your baby to sleep. Always remember to read the label and administer the right dose for your baby's age.

For the **gurgle** video on **How to ease the pain of teething**, go to **gurgle.com** and click on **Videos**

SHE'S GOT A COLD OR A TEMPERATURE
Similarly, babies with a runny nose or a temperature will tend to wake more often in the night, and there's little you can do except administer the usual medication to try and bring down her temperature. Check that she is not dehydrated, and give her a little water or diluted juice if necessary. Aromatic inhalents should not be used in babies less than three months old, and should be used with care in older babies and young children. A single drop on a tissue in the room is sufficient.

SHE'S HUNGRY
Of course, don't discount the obvious. She may be genuinely hungry, in which case you might want to try and give a slightly larger feed before she goes to sleep in the hope that this will tide her over. Some babies simply have large appetites and even the onset of solids might not be enough to get them through the night at this stage. Formula-fed babies tend to sleep through more readily than breastfed babies, simply because breast milk, being easier to digest, passes through their system more quickly. So if you are feeding your baby a mixture of breast and bottle, you may find that a formula feed last thing at night fills her up enough to make her sleep through.

For the **gurgle** video on **Making up a bottle**, go to **gurgle.com** and click on **Videos**

Mum's top tip

My doctor chastised me earlier this week for allowing my baby to wrap me round her little finger! I had admitted that she was still waking in the night for a couple of feeds and that I was obliging. I explained that my baby did seem genuinely hungry as she would feed well for at least ten minutes, but the doctor seemed to think I was making a rod for my back – yes, that old chestnut that we mums hear all the time.

I was so unnerved by my doctor's approach, and her insistence that if I didn't stop these feeds before my baby was eight months old, I would be in for sleepless nights for over two years, that I spoke to a few health visitors and mothers that I am in contact with through breastfeeding support groups. Not one of these supported my doctor's view – including those with older children who had had similar experiences to mine.

I quickly made the decision to continue with 'baby-led weaning' and breastfeeding on demand as it was the best for my baby and wasn't causing me any problems. After all, a 10–15-minute feed in the night isn't exactly a massive issue as she goes straight back to sleep. Funnily enough, just after making that decision my baby has started sleeping longer at night and only waking up for one feed.

I am now a firm believer in listening to your baby and your instincts. Yet again, this experience proves to me that babies will reach each stage of development in their own time. I hope this message is helpful to any other mothers out there who are being encouraged to ignore their instincts and force development onto their baby.

Getting your evenings back!

Putting a baby to bed at night can be one of the most tiring times of the day for parents. It's when you want to put your feet up and have a bit of a rest, or just get on and do the things (you know, exciting stuff like washing and ironing) that have been piling up. But if your baby doesn't settle, those dreams of dinner at the table with your other half can seem unreachable and you feel cheated out of a precious bit of 'you' time.

At six months

There are, however, ways to make bedtime a little bit easier for all concerned. Most parents decide it's time to put their baby in his own room at about six months. By this stage, he needs around 14 hours of sleep (we can all dream of such luxury), including a solid 12 hours at night (see pages 16–19).

Your baby will probably have a short morning nap and then about two hours at lunchtime. If he misses these, a short nap (20–30 minutes) before his evening meal should stop him becoming overtired at bedtime.

Most children this age are on three meals a day plus a couple of milk feeds. Make sure your baby isn't drinking too much milk during the day as this will mean he will eat fewer solids and will be more likely to wake up hungry during the night.

If your six-month-old has decided he doesn't like settling down for the night, don't give up. He will get used to it. You won't be scarring him for ever if you stick to your guns. The easiest way to settle a baby is a 'light' version of controlled crying (see pages 144–9). Never fear: this is not the 'leave him screaming for hours and just use bigger earplugs' method. This is a gentle but firm way of showing that you love him but he's going to stay in the cot all night.

Putting it into practice

How to go about it? Well, go through your usual routine – bath, milk, story – and then put him in his cot, say goodnight and walk out of the room.

- If your baby cries, don't be tempted to rush in and comfort him. Step back into the room, make soothing noises and, after a minute or so, walk away again.
- If your baby doesn't settle, leave him for five minutes and then return to his room.
- Don't pick him up, no matter how tempting, and try to not make eye contact.
- Don't speak to your baby but make calming noises and gently stroke his forehead or any other place you know he finds comforting. After two minutes, leave the room.
- If he's still crying, leave him for ten minutes before going back in. Repeat the same process until he settles.

Very few babies need more than two visits at bedtime. Once they realize that they aren't going to be picked up, cuddled and get a change of scenery, they get bored of making a fuss and conclude that, yes, they are indeed very tired and a nice night's sleep would be just the ticket.

It's sometimes tempting to try to feed your baby to sleep with a bottle, but this can be a hard habit to break, so although it might be a quick fix, it can lead to a long battle to get him to sleep without it again.

It is never too early to put good sleep habits into place. If you rock your baby to sleep, play or sing a soothing lullaby or use a dummy to help him nod off, he will become dependent on these rituals. Helping your baby to drift off naturally from a young age will mean he'll be more able to get himself back to sleep on his own if he wakes up in the night. (For more on sleep comfort habits, see pages 150–55.)

Mum's top tip

For the first couple of weeks, my newborn baby slept much better during the day than at night. Luckily, my husband shared the night-time feeds and cuddles. I began to do more things with him during the day – talking to him and playing with him, even leaving the TV or radio on when he was asleep. I think that he soon began to know the difference between day and night. It takes at least 3–4 weeks to get any kind of routine in place, so just stick with it and make sure you sleep whenever your baby does. Good luck!

Happy bedtimes: 6–18 months

Your baby at six months

By month six, you will notice your baby becoming more of a little person, as she masters sitting, prefers to be upright and starts trying to tell you things with gestures, body language and eye contact.

It is hard to believe she is halfway through her first year now and has already come such a long way. Important changes will be taking place during this month too. Most babies start experimenting with solids at around this age, and as experts recommend babies sleep in a cot in their parents' room for at least the first six months, you might be moving your baby into a room of her own soon. (See page 137 for advice on moving your baby into a cot, and page 122 for moving her into her own room.)

HEARING

At around six months, your baby will turn to listen to very quiet noises if there are no distractions in the room. If she hears your voice, even from some distance away, she will turn to find you.

SITTING

She may be able to sit unsupported for a while as her limbs, neck and back muscles become much stronger. Remember that she may still topple over from time to time when gravity gets the better of her, so don't leave her without cushions to support her or something soft on the floor to fall onto.

GRASPING

Your baby may start to show interest in objects placed around her. She may even reach out to grasp them or twist her body to get at an object behind her. Once she has grasped it, she might try to pass it from one hand to the next. She can properly play with toys now, but don't go crazy buying every new thing on the market – she will be happy enough banging away with a wooden spoon and some pots and pans. Everything goes into her mouth at this stage, so be careful to keep anything that poses a choking hazard away from her reach.

UNDERSTANDING THE WORLD

Your baby will be able to distinguish between different emotions and facial expressions and may get excited when you are happy or become upset if you are sad. She is also starting to understand where things are in relation to her, so if something is out of sight, she can move to see it, and if an object is hidden in her toybox, she may attempt to find it.

Six-month-olds also love to mimic you. Try playing peek-a-boo by putting your hands up to your face and she will probably try to join in. Poking your tongue out and blowing raspberries has never been so much fun.

BEHAVIOUR

It may be a good idea to get into the habit of praising your baby for good behaviour and saying a firm 'No' if she goes to tug at an electrical wire, for instance. Try not to get too frustrated with her if she goes for things she shouldn't, as she needs to experiment and does not yet know what is off limits.

Sleep patterns at six months

By the age of six months, your baby is developing at a great pace. His interest in the world around him and his awareness of his own body are growing as his concentration increases. It is possible that he will be able to roll or sit up unaided now and he may also learn to crawl at this stage.

Your baby makes sounds to get your attention and likes to stretch out his arms to be picked up by you. Teething is likely to begin around this time and, as far as daytime sleeping goes, he may need only two naps during the day.

How much sleep

Although it is feasible that your baby will be sleeping through the night in a continuous block of time by this age, it won't necessarily be the case for every child, and your baby may still be having broken nights of sleep.

While this may be frustrating for parents who are fighting exhaustion and longing for a good night's sleep, it is also perfectly normal. And it won't last for ever. Between six and 12 months of age, your baby will start to sleep for longer periods of time. By 12 months, his sleeping patterns may well have regulated and he should be sleeping all the way through the night.

At any rate, your baby will probably have dropped his third daytime nap by six months, requiring only two naps during the day. As an average guide, your baby's sleep needs at six months will amount to about 14 hours over any 24-hour period. This includes 10–12 hours at night, and 2–4 hours spread between two, or possibly three, naps during the day (see pages 16–19).

How often to feed during the night

Unless there are any medical issues or concerns over weight gain that your health visitor or GP has flagged up, it is possible to wean your baby off night-time feeds at this stage of his development. It is likely that you are feeding your baby some solids now, in addition to milk, and he is therefore receiving plenty of nutrients to keep him going at night.

If you are breastfeeding, you may wish to continue with night feeds, especially at around 11pm or midnight, as for some women this means gaining extra time in bed in the morning. It really depends on what works best for you and your baby. If you do want to wean your baby off night-time feeds, just check first that there aren't any other issues, such as teething, going on at the same time. It is best to focus on one thing at a time.

Mum's top tip

As babies get older they sleep less and want to interact with people more. During the day, I started to sit my baby in a bouncy chair so that he could watch what was going on, or I would play with him when he started to cry rather than just offering the breast or bottle. I made sure he had plenty of things to look at when he was awake. When he started reaching out to play with his baby gym, he seemed much happier.

Weaning your baby from a night-time feed can be challenging for a few days, but if you are firm, you'll succeed. Offering your baby a feed before bedtime and then a bottle of sterilized water to drink if he wakes during the night is one way to tackle a waking baby who wants a feed. Although if your baby has only ever breastfed and has never taken a bottle before, it can be another issue trying to get him to suck from a teat.

If you are happy with your baby waking up in the night for a feed, there is no need to try and change things. But if you are finding it hard to wean him off his night-time feed, consult your health visitor for advice suited to your individual circumstances.

What's a good sleep routine

Consistency is a must for establishing a good sleeping routine for your baby. Trying to keep his sleep periods to the same time each day will help set his body clock. At the same time, though, it is important not to inflict a nap on your baby when he is clearly not tired. Some days he might not need his morning nap until 11am; on others he will be showing signs that he needs one at 10am. You need to accommodate your baby's needs while at the same time establishing a fairly predictable routine.

The winding-down period before naps and bedtime is also crucial, so make sure this phase isn't rushed. Relaxing and calming your baby with a bath, soothing music or songs, and of course plenty of cuddles and perhaps a gentle massage, all aid the settling-down process. If possible, try to do these things in a similar order each time, so that he knows what's coming next.

If your baby is waking up during the night, make sure a good bedtime routine is established. It might also be worth changing his bedtime. If he is overtired or overstimulated, it could upset his body clock and cause him to be restless and wakeful during the night. Putting him to bed slightly earlier, before he gets too tired, can have a dramatic effect, and he may soon be sleeping through the night.

How development affects sleep patterns

It is worth noting that your baby's developmental changes could well have an effect on his sleeping patterns. He may be very excited about using newfound skills such as sitting or crawling.

Indeed, your baby may start to wake up early in order to practise them. He is learning so many new things each day that he will be determined to implement them as often as possible.

Milestones such as learning to crawl might also impact on daytime naps as it can be difficult to get your baby to slow down when so much is going on. Ironically, this is the time he needs his naps the most, as he is having so much physical exercise.

Separation anxiety may also rear its head around this age (see pages 136–7). Your baby will be hovering uncertainly between excitement over his new independence and fear over the growing realization that he is apart from you in a way he wasn't conscious of previously.

Another cause of sleep disruption is, of course, the start of teething. If your baby is cutting a tooth, sleep is bound to be interrupted. After all, he is going to be experiencing some pain. It is best not to try and solve sleep issues while your baby is going through the teething process. You should consider using some over-the-counter children's pain relief at bedtime or consult a qualified homeopathic doctor for a suitable alternative. (For more on teething and sleep, see page 170.)

Mum's top tip

When my little one was teething, I found the best thing was a gel-filled teething ring that you could put in the fridge to make it especially cooling and comforting. That and some homeopathic granules, rubbed gently onto his gums with my little finger. And lots of patience and cuddles. It soon passes!

Your guide to sleep routines: 6–12 months

Six-month-old babies need around 14 hours' sleep, which roughly equates to two to four hours in the day and 10–12 hours at night. These aren't continuous hours of sleep, however, and your baby may nap for two, possibly three, hours or in a series of smaller naps throughout the day and night.

No baby, toddler, child, teenager or adult is the same when it comes to sleep, so resist the urge to compare your baby's sleep patterns with anyone else's. This is also a very rough estimate as some babies need very little sleep while others sleep for much longer. If you are worried about your baby's sleep patterns, consult your health visitor or GP for advice.

New bedroom

If your baby is still sleeping in your room, you are probably getting tired of creeping in at midnight and stubbing your toes on the furniture. Experts recommend that babies sleep in a cot in their parents' room until they are at least six months old, so now might be a good time to think about moving your baby into her own room. It is best to do this around six, seven or eight months as the older your baby gets the more she is aware of (and likes) being in your room and it becomes increasingly hard to move her.

top tips

Tips for a moving your baby into her own room

There is a good chance your baby will take to her own room instantly and settle down without complaint. In fact you will probably miss having her in your room more than she will. Here are **gurgle's** top tips to help you through the move:

- Start on a Friday night, so if you do have a couple of sleepless nights you'll have the weekend to recover.
- Try to spend lots of playtime in your baby's bedroom before you move her, so she is familiar with it and enjoys spending time in there.
- Make sure you make the area around her cot as similar as possible to the environment she was used to, using the same mobiles, cot bumpers or music you played to her every night. Keep to the same bedtime routine as before.
- Resist the urge to put her back in your room if things get tough. It might take a few broken nights for her to get used to her room, but she'll get the hang of it and will be a lot less disturbed by you than she was when sleeping with you.

top tips

Dropping a nap

If you notice your baby fussing during daytime naps, falling asleep then waking again soon after, or being reluctant to sleep at night, she may need to drop a nap. Most children drop from two naps to one around their first birthday, but don't rush your baby into it if she isn't ready.

Which nap should I drop?

Rather than dropping the morning nap altogether, try making it later, say about 12–1pm. That way your baby will hopefully have a longer nap (an hour to an hour and a half) and can probably make it through to bedtime with no further sleep.

HOW DO I GO ABOUT THIS?

Move the morning nap back by 15 minutes each day until you reach the desired nap time. Some babies will take only a few days to adjust, especially if they were ready to drop the nap; others may take a few weeks and will still need a short nap in the afternoon for a week or so. If this is the case, keep the nap short and try not to make it too late.

DROPPING THE LAST NAP

Most children need a daily nap until they are around three years old, and some continue to have naps until they are five. Dropping from one nap to none is much the same as dropping from two to one, and your child will display the same signs as before (wakefulness during her nap or at night). As before, try shortening the daytime nap by 15 minutes over a period of time until eventually she has no nap. Most children still need a 'quiet time' in the afternoon, however, so that their minds and bodies have a chance to relax.

When your baby is unwell

If your baby is unwell, it will have a knock-on effect on his sleep patterns. How these are affected depends on what the problem is. If he has a tummy bug, for example, he may wake several times in the night because he's feeling sick or has stomach cramps. If he is feverish and running a high temperature, he may appear more sluggish and exhausted than usual and want to do nothing but sleep!

Of course, normal rules don't apply when your baby is ill and you shouldn't leave him to cry as you might if he wasn't sick. But beware that an older child doesn't use this as a bargaining tool, playing the 'Mummy, my tummy hurts – I need a cuddle!' card when he's fit and well again.

If you're concerned that your baby might be sick during the night and he sleeps in his own room, it's advisable to bring his cot into your room so that you can monitor him throughout the night.

- Put a bucket by the side of the bed and keep a towel to hand in case you need them in an emergency.
- Keep a mug of water – or a bottle of boiled, cooled water for a younger baby – nearby for your child to sip on during the night.

- Rest is often the best medicine if your child is feeling under the weather, as he may not have the energy to do much else. But, of course, if you have any concerns about your child's health, always consult your doctor.

- Try not to worry too much if your baby's sleeping patterns are affected, as these disruptions will normally be temporary and your child should return to his normal sleeping habits once he's back to full health.

Once you are reassured that he is better, it's advisable to adopt the same firm tactics as recommended in 'How to deal with a wakeful baby' (see overleaf). Don't rush to him every time he cries, but try to encourage him to settle himself back to sleep. It may take a little time to get your baby's sleep patterns back on track; just remember to keep to a minimum the amount of interaction you have with him at night, so that he soon realizes there's little to be gained from getting up in the early hours.

Mum's top tip

I found that I needed to re-educate my baby about sleep routines once she had recovered from being unwell. It's natural to break all the rules and go to your baby as soon as she cries when you know she is unwell but as soon as she is better, my advice is to go back to your routine. You'll be surprised how quickly the old sleep routines return if you are firm.

How to deal with a wakeful baby

We all know that one of the biggest adjustments you need to make when you have a new baby is learning to cope with a lack of sleep. It's enough to drive anyone to distraction!

It has to be said that the phrase 'to sleep like a baby' usually doesn't apply, and while you may have friends whose babies are absolute angels and sleep through the night from day one, be reassured that this is rarely the case. Although there's no magic wand you can wave to make your baby sleep through the night, don't despair as there are ways in which you can help to improve the situation.

Mum's top tip

Controlled crying works for some people, but it depends on the baby. I tried it with my baby Dylan but he cried as if he was in the most terrible pain, and despite leaving him for more than 20 minutes (which felt like an eternity!), he never showed any signs of easing off. Perhaps you do just have to be strong and see it through, but I certainly wasn't able to. That said, there have been times during the day when the crying has got too much for me and I have put him down in his cot for a few minutes just for me to breathe and count to ten!

Why do babies wake in the night?

Newborns tend to wake several times a night for the first few weeks as their tummies are small and can only cope with small amounts of milk at a time and they therefore need to be fed little and often. As babies get older, their stomachs become larger and they can therefore take more in food at any one time. As a result, they are satisfied for longer and can sleep for longer periods.

Other reasons for waking in the night could include illness, being too hot or too cold, a dirty nappy or an uncomfortable sleepsuit – the list is endless. What's for sure, though, is the minute your baby wakes up, there's no way he's going to suffer in silence!

WHAT TO DO

While there are those who believe that you should run to your baby the moment he wakes, others think it's better to leave your baby for a while. The latter approach is known as controlled crying and is covered in greater detail on pages 144–9. This generally shouldn't be applied until your baby is six months old.

You may want to try letting your baby cry for small periods of time to ascertain whether he can settle of his own accord. If he thinks that every time he wakes you will go to him, then he will keep crying until he gets your attention. Obviously, if he's becoming increasingly distressed and continues to cry for an extended period of time, then settle him with a brief cuddle, but don't turn any lights on or talk to him as he may well only be half awake and this will merely make him too excited to go back to sleep.

Of course it's a personal decision and it may take a few days or even a week for your baby to get used to the fact that you won't come running the minute he cries, but ultimately he will be more likely to sleep through the night.

Your baby at 12 months

From now on, your baby's independence will shine through. She no longer sits still at story time or stays quiet while you try to dress her. Once she has started walking, being picked up or cooped up inside the house will frustrate her no end, so have some standby activities that use up a bit of toddler energy if you are stuck indoors.

She will now know what she does and doesn't want and will assert herself in her own unique way (usually clamping her mouth shut when she has had enough food, or wriggling out of a cuddle). Don't despair: there will be quiet times when all your baby wants to do is rest from exploring or walking and sit on your lap, snuggling into your arms. Now is the time to look at your amazing child – she's maybe walking, perhaps attempting a few words, and growing bigger, stronger and more independent every day. This is definitely a time to celebrate how far you've come!

At the age of 12 months, your child is on the brink of toddlerhood. As you watch her tearing around the place like a tornado, you probably realize that things will never be quite the same again.

In fact, the biggest challenge can often be in encouraging your child to slow down and get some sleep. Daytime naps can suddenly lose their appeal and she might be more anxious about being separated from you than she was before. So let's take a look at some of the issues concerning sleep and your one-year-old.

Your guide to sleep routines: 12–18 months

By the time your baby is 12 months old, it is likely she will be sleeping through the night in one uninterrupted session. As both crawling and learning to walk use up large amounts of energy, night sleeps will become an important recovery time for your child. However, all children are individual and some babies just seem to be more wakeful than others. If your baby falls into this category, don't despair, but try to accept that she is developing at her own rate.

As a rule, babies of 12 months will be sleeping for about 12–14 hours in any 24-hour period. This will consist of something in the region of 11–12 hours at night and one or two naps during the day of about one and a half to three hours in total (see pages 16–19).

Your child will probably be able to stay awake for between three and four hours from first waking to first nap time and then the same length of time until her second nap. Some children will already have progressed from two daytime naps to one, in which case they may be able to stay awake for five to six hours, although you may need to bring bedtime forward a little to facilitate this change.

You will know if your child is getting enough sleep by charting her energy levels and corresponding behaviour during the day. For example, if she is sleeping only ten hours a night but doesn't seem grumpy and overly tired during the day, that's fine. There is no point trying to change things if they are working for you both. If, on the other hand, she wakes up in the morning after ten hours' sleep still tired or gets extremely grumpy before her mid-morning nap, then you will know she needs more sleep at night.

Typical sleeping pattern at 12 months

Wake-up time: 7am

First nap: 10.30am–12pm

Second nap: 3–4pm

Bedtime: 7–8pm

Mum's top tip

I encouraged my baby to have a longer morning nap and a shorter afternoon nap. That way I was sure he was getting the sleep hours he needed, but he wasn't sleeping so much in the afternoon that he was still wide awake at bedtime. Don't be tempted to let your baby sleep later in the afternoon, even if it does buy you some peace or a chance to catch up on things. Gently wake him up (he's done it to you often enough, after all!) and distract him by playing with him or going out for a walk in the buggy. A bit of fresh air in the afternoon often makes for better night-time sleep.

Top tips at 12–18 months

From 12 months your baby is more like a toddler and, as such, is much more mobile and will be learning to play. He will be developing rapidly and his mind and body will be working incredibly hard. This stage can be tricky, as your child may feel he needs more sleep in the afternoon, and can become overtired and cranky if he doesn't get it. But the problem is that if he sleeps any later than about 3pm he will not be tired at night. At this age, your child usually needs 12–14 hours sleep a day, with 11–12 of these at night and a nap at lunchtime.

- Do your best to make sure your child gets a nap at lunchtime, and if he starts getting cranky in the afternoon, sit down with him and read a book together to give him a bit of a rest.

- Try putting him to bed a little earlier, bearing in mind that he will wake up a bit earlier as a result. Think of an earlier morning as a trade-off against a smoother bedtime routine in which he won't be overtired at the end of the day.

- If you're no longer breastfeeding but your child is still waking in the night and demanding a feed, you can break the habit by diluting some formula milk with water for every feed. Pretty soon he'll be on plain water and not want it any more.

Getting into a good sleeping routine

A good bedtime routine at this age is essential for your child to get a good night's rest. Taking the time each evening to help him wind down after a busy day is very important. Parents who get frustrated and cross because they can't understand why a quick change into a sleepsuit and kiss on the cheek doesn't seem to be settling their child will benefit from slowing everything down a little.

Try to avoid overstimulating your child. Young children usually find a bath relaxing and it might be a good idea to incorporate this into your child's bedtime routine. Similarly, a story, singing a song or playing some music, or gently stroking his forehead while he has his last feed can work wonders at calming his spirits (although don't forget that he will need to have his teeth brushed if his last feed or drink is anything other than water).

Separation anxiety

If your child is finding it difficult to settle even when you have established a good bedtime routine, it could be that he is experiencing separation anxiety. His feelings of separateness from you are exacerbated by all the new skills he is acquiring at this time. While crawling, walking and talking, and countless other new skills and experiences, all demonstrate his growing independence, they also highlight for him how separate you are from each other.

If your child seems fairly secure during the day, then it may be that he just needs a bit of extra time with you before going to bed. This could mean creating an extra ten minutes or so, just to stay with him as he gets ready to go to sleep. Giving him a cuddle and holding him for a while is perfectly acceptable, but make sure you don't fall into the trap of staying with him until he's asleep.

If, however, you are experiencing clinginess from your child during the day, especially when you leave the room or at bedtime, then separation anxiety might be an issue. The best way to tackle this is during his waking hours. Make sure that you always tell him when you are leaving the room and then make a fuss of him when you return. Play in his room so that he doesn't just regard it as a place to be away from you, and give him a special toy to comfort him when you're not there.

You could also put some photographs of yourself on the walls or in a small baby-friendly book that will offer reassurance to your child when you're not around. And start the bedtime routine earlier so that you have more time to hold, chat to and cuddle him as he winds down for the night. This also means you will be less likely to rush bedtimes – much more enjoyable for everyone!

When should my child move into a cot?

Depending on whether you have been co-sleeping with him up to this point, you might decide that this is the right age to move your child into a cot at night.

- If this is the first time you have used a cot, try it first for your child's daytime naps to allow him to get used to it.
- Make sure you recreate the secure environment he is leaving behind: special blankets and soft toys are important, as are mobiles and perhaps photos of you.
- Although the risk of cot death (or SIDS, see pages 48–53) is greatly reduced at this age, remember that he should be placed on his back with his feet touching the end of the cot.
- Don't allow him to get overheated (see pages 92–3) and avoid tucking him in too tightly, so that he can throw off his bedclothes if he does get too hot.
- You may feel happier with a baby monitor – especially one with talkback on the roaming monitor – to enable you to offer words of reassurance to your child.

For the **gurgle** video on **Moving from a cot to a bed**, go to **gurgle.com** and click on **Videos**

Troubleshooting: sleep and your baby

Creating a relaxed sleeping environment

When attempting to establish a bedtime routine, it's worth giving some thought as to how you can create a soothing, calming environment for your baby so that he's in the right frame of mind to go to sleep – and stay asleep!

top tips

- Try to eliminate any distractions or anything that might make him hyper in the run-up to bedtime.
- Don't let your baby watch television or a DVD just before bed. Aside from making him overexcited, it might mean that his sleep patterns throughout the night will be disrupted and he could experience nightmares if, perhaps, he had watched a programme with a scary character in it.
- As your child gets older, bear in mind that it's inadvisable to have a computer or television in his room as it encourages anti-social behaviour. Watching television and playing computer games should be closely monitored until your child reaches his teenage years.
- Read your baby a relaxing bedtime story. Not only is he more likely to have a peaceful night's sleep, but it's a great chance for the two of you to spend some quality time together.
- Another option is to play some calming music – something classical, maybe, or perhaps a lullaby.
- Remember that your main aim is to ensure that your baby is relaxed and calm before bed, so that, with luck, all the family will get a good night's rest.

When your baby won't sleep

Do you remember those halcyon days when you had a wonderful eight uninterrupted hours of sleep a night? How on earth can you get a good night's kip when you have a crying baby who scarcely sleeps for more than an hour at a time? And what if he simply won't go to sleep during the day? Read on to find out how to troubleshoot your baby's wakefulness so that everyone gets some much needed shuteye.

Babies are individuals and, like older people, sleep for varying amounts of time, depending on their personal requirements. What all babies have in common, however, is that they need *lots* of sleep, including proper naps during the day. If they are not napping during the day, this could indicate a problem that needs addressing.

You may be trying to dictate a routine to your baby that is not fitting in with his natural sleep rhythms and therefore confusing his sleep cycle. Don't try to impose strict nap times on a young baby. Instead, it's best to respond to the signals that your baby gives you to show you that he's tired and wants to sleep. Learn about how to establish a good bedtime routine (see pages 62–5). If you're still unable to fathom why your baby won't nap, you should consult your health visitor.

Questions to ask yourself

It might be that your baby is overtired. If he is not sleeping well at night, this could affect daytime naps. Ask yourself the following:

- Is he overtired because he's very hungry at night and often wakes to feed? If so, perhaps you could try to increase his feed prior to bedtime. If he is still under three months old, it will be difficult to dictate the terms of feeding, as he's still too young and his stomach very small. Try to wait until you get past three months before you worry about routines and sleeping. Once your baby hits the six-month mark, when solids will have been introduced, he will need less milk and it will therefore be easier to reduce night feeds.

- Is your baby overtired because he's waking up too early? Maybe the room he's sleeping in is too light or the temperature isn't right – it's too warm or too cold. Try using blackout blinds to keep the morning at bay and ensure that your baby has appropriate covers to keep him warm or cool enough (see page 52). Maybe he's also the sort of baby who intensely dislikes having a dirty nappy. If so, try changing him during the night or using more absorbent nappies. Some parents also swear that gentle background sound helps babies sleep better.

- Could your baby be overstimulated? Is there too much going on in his immediate environment prior to his nap time? Visitors, noisy radio or TV programmes or indeed any unusual activity that might arouse his interest could be stopping him from having a nap. If this is the case, ensure that he has a quiet wind-down period before he is put down for a nap. Just as at bedtime, establishing a bit of a routine is helpful for encouraging your baby to sleep. In addition, make sure he has a quiet, comfortable place to sleep during the day.

What is controlled crying?

How well your baby is (or isn't) sleeping affects the whole family. A baby that needs you to stay with her until she falls asleep can really disrupt your evenings. If she is less dependent on you at night, this will allow you more freedom and some well-earned space. You'll feel more relaxed and able to wind down in the evenings and more confident about leaving your child with friends or family should you want (or need!) a night out.

The controlled crying technique (CCT) essentially teaches your baby to fall asleep by herself by intermittently both reassuring her of your presence and leaving her alone in her cot for timed intervals.

Although CCT sometimes attracts a bad press, its beneficial effects when properly implemented are well documented. Australian researchers found that teaching mothers CCT reduced their babies' sleep problems over two months. Moreover, it also appeared to help women who reported symptoms of depression, according to findings published in the *British Medical Journal*.

If your baby needs your presence to fall asleep (or any other sleep aid, such as milk or dummies), then CCT might be the answer. Mandy Gurney, founder of Millpond Children's Sleep Clinic and author of *Teach Your Child to Sleep*, sounds a word of caution, however. 'You cannot make a child sleep, you can only provide the right conditions,' she says. 'It should never happen that babies are left crying for hours. It is important to recognize there are a whole range of sleep techniques and CCT may not always be appropriate.' This technique is not suitable for babies under six months who are waking for night feeds, and should never be used when a child has a temperature or where there is an anxiety-based sleep problem.

Is it right for my baby?

CCT should only be used for babies who are at least six months old. Mandy Gurney counsels parents to think about their particular circumstances before commencing CCT. 'It is very important to sit down and think things through, or the crying will be wasted,' she says. If you're thinking of starting CCT, first consider the following:

DO WE HAVE AN APPROPRIATE BEDTIME ROUTINE IN PLACE?
This should be a gentle winding down that focuses on the place the child sleeps, and is as quiet and calm as possible. The hour before bedtime should be a peaceful one. Splashing around with your child in the bath beforehand, for example, is not a good prelude for settling her down to sleep.

ARE MY BABY'S DAYTIME NAPS WELL STRUCTURED?
It is important that your baby sleeps during the day at the correct times. She shouldn't be sleeping too close to bedtime, or having too much or too little sleep. If your baby's nap routine is not in good order, then she may be overtired, grizzly and difficult to handle, which is not the best starting point for CCT.

IS SHE DEPENDENT ON OUTSIDE CUES TO GET HER TO SLEEP?
If your baby is dependent on milk, dummies, rocking or parental presence to get her to sleep, then CCT is appropriate. If your child is anxious about going to sleep or if you don't really want to do CCT and are merely following well-meaning advice from other people, then it's not the technique for you.

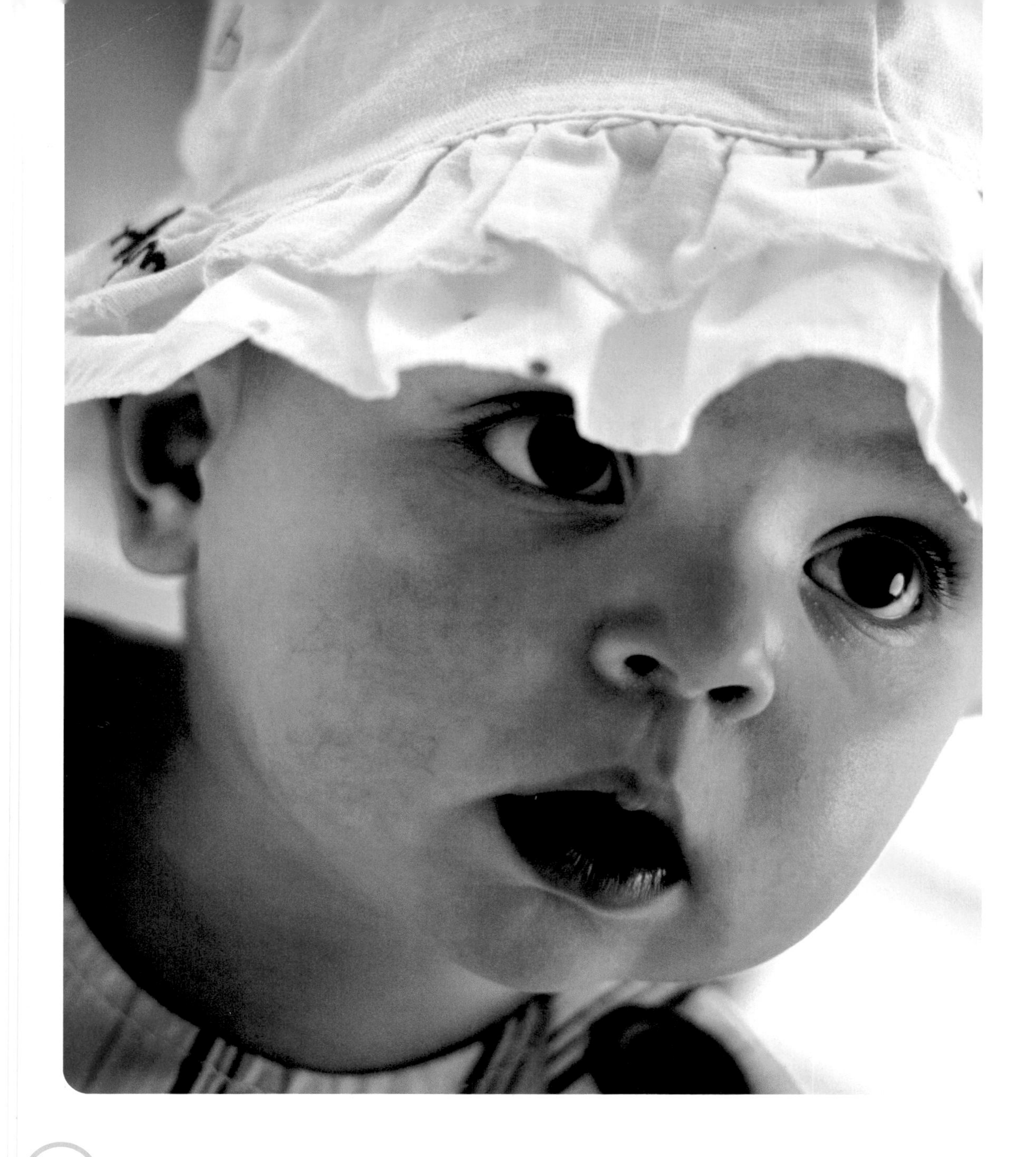

You should not attempt CCT with a child who is:

- Younger than six months (CCT is not for young babies who wake for night feeds).
- Not sleeping in a cot.
- Not weaned from night feeds (CCT is only appropriate for healthy, well-grown babies).

Your baby should also be:

- Eating and drinking as normal for her age during the day.
- Well (with no temperature or any other problem, such as teething).

Mandy Gurney advises working parents to start CCT on a Friday night, adding wryly: 'It might also be a good idea to warn the neighbours!'

Putting the technique into practice

Having established a good bedtime routine in the run-up to starting CCT, and having checked the above list for to see whether the technique is right for you, you are now ready to try CCT for yourself.

- When your baby is ready to go to sleep, put her in the cot and say goodnight. Leave the room and wait. Your baby will probably start crying.
- Wait five minutes before going back into the room (or you may wish to start at two minutes and then double the time from there on).
- When you go back into the room, DON'T pick up your baby. This is very important. If you do, it will defeat the object of the exercise, sending out the message: 'If you cry long enough, Mummy will come and cuddle you.'

- You should merely pop back in, say your baby's name and 'Mummy's here, go to sleep', before leaving the room.
- This time wait for ten minutes before going back in (or four minutes if you started on two, if you're more comfortable with that).
- The third time, wait for 15 minutes. If your baby still hasn't settled, don't increase this gap. Keep going in at 15-minute intervals. Eventually she will go to sleep.
- If at any point during the proceedings you notice a change in volume, pause and wait to see if your baby starts to 'cry down'. If her crying does start to decrease in volume, don't go back in. Only if she starts to cry more loudly again should you re-enter the room.

Prepare yourself before you start

Prepare for the first three nights to be horrendous. 'If you think about it,' says Mandy Gurney, 'the only way a baby can communicate distress is through crying. If you were used to falling asleep in a certain way and that's taken away, you wouldn't be able to go to sleep without a struggle either.'

Remember that your baby knows you are there. You are simply going back to check and reassure her of your presence. For parents who are worried about the possible negative psychological effects CCT may be inflicting upon their child, Gurney has this analogy:

'If you were stuck in traffic on a motorway with your baby strapped into a car seat behind you and she wanted your attention, you wouldn't get out of the car and take your baby out of her seat.

'You would of course comfort and reassure her from the front seat. At the end of the journey, you wouldn't think you had caused your baby psychological damage because she had been kept in her seat. It is the same principle with CCT; you are regularly reassuring your baby but without touching or picking her up.'

One of the best things about CCT is how quickly results can be achieved. The first three nights are likely to be the most testing but after that things usually get better fast.

Dunstan Bruce and his wife Daisy used CCT on their first child, Lola, who is now at primary school.

'We're light sleepers, so we needed her out of our bedroom and sleeping alone as soon as possible, although listening to her crying was difficult at first, we persevered and it worked within a week.'

It is important that parents implementing CCT feel supported. It is crucial to be able to share the burden of what will potentially be a rather challenging few days. If one person is attempting to carry out CCT alone, then it's very easy to lose heart and give in, in which case all the hard work will have been for nothing.

Gabriella Jacobs, 41, says her partner Dave is to thank for the way the couple's seven-month-old twin girls settle down at night.

'Controlled crying was incredibly difficult at first,' she remembers. 'When you have not one but two babies crying, the sound is horrendous – and totally heart-wrenching. It was all I could do to stop myself running in there after 30 seconds and gathering them up in my arms.

'But Dave was really tough. He said if we kept going in, we would regret it for the next goodness knows how many years. We had to be firm.

'Now, none of my friends can believe how good the twins are – especially those with young babies themselves. I have to say, it was the toughest thing to do, but it did pay off.'

It is clear that CCT can be a very helpful technique if used in the right circumstances. When all's said and done, you know your baby better than anyone else. If you feel that CCT could benefit you and your baby and help her to settle at night, then you could give it a try. Just ensure that you and your baby are ready before you embark on it.

Should you encourage sleep comfort habits?

A comfort habit or object is something that literally helps soothe and relax your baby. It can be anything from a dummy to a beloved toy or blanket. Everyone has a different opinion about whether comfort habits are a good or bad idea. As with anything, they have their advantages and disadvantages.

Many people believe that developing comfort habits can reassure young children and be generally beneficial: not only can they help children get to sleep, but they can help them through any stressful times, providing reassurance and – as the name suggests – comfort.

The dummy question

Opinion is split over whether or not dummies are a good idea. Some people object to them as they fear children may become overly reliant on them; others believe they are unhygienic. Occasionally, dummies can cause dermatitis around the mouth and, although they can help a child to fall asleep, if the child becomes too reliant on the dummy and it falls out, sleeping patterns might then be disrupted.

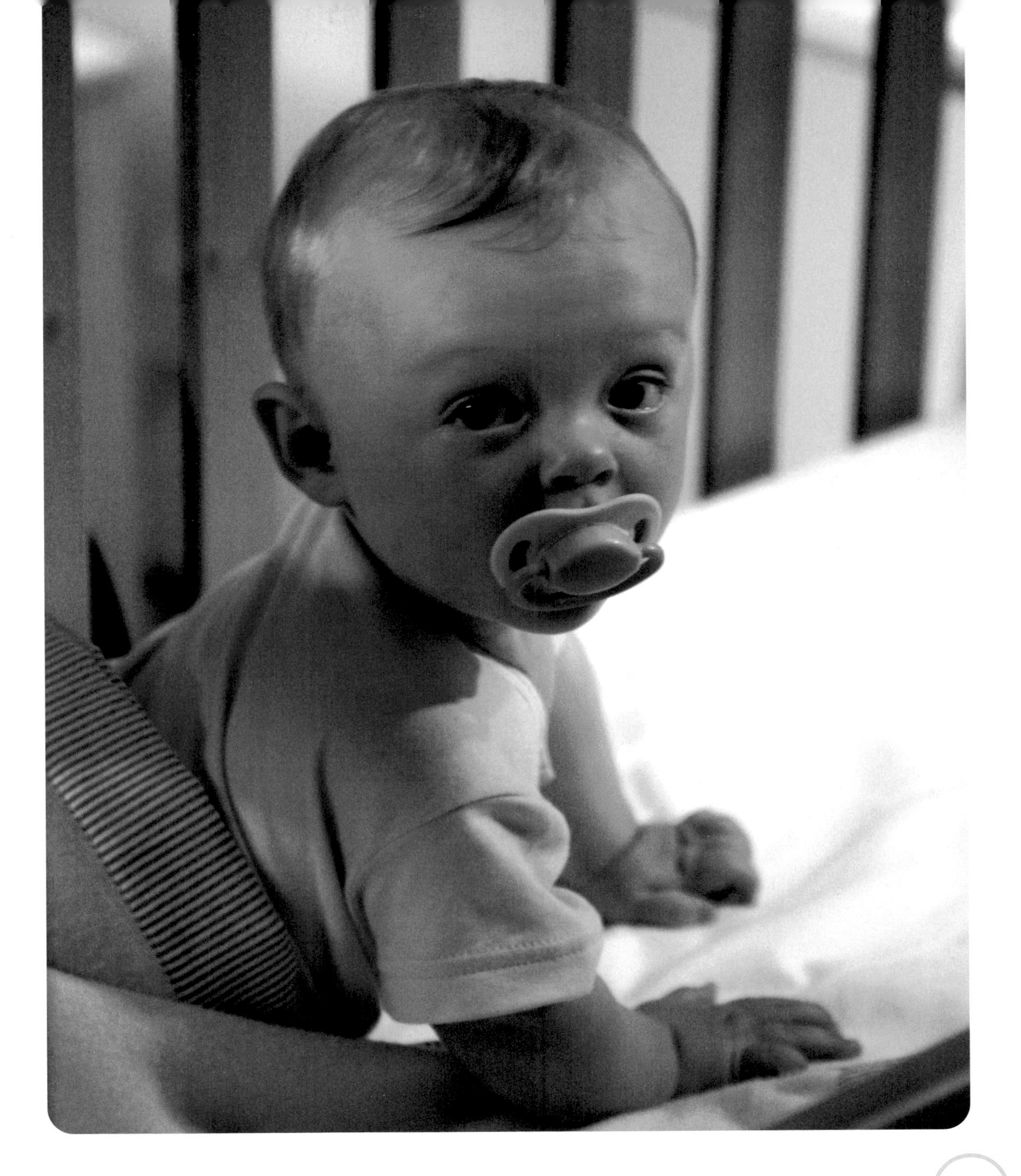

There is also a school of thought that dummies damage children's teeth, although if a child doesn't use a dummy past the toddler years the risks are fairly minimal. In the short term, however, dummies aren't likely to cause any harm. Indeed, as they can help your baby to go to sleep, a bedtime routine might be more readily established using one. Having said that, it's advisable to stop your child using a dummy by the age of three. He is likely to go through a period of missing the dummy and pining for it, but this will happen at whatever stage you wean him off it.

Dummies and breastfeeding

There is a view that dummies can put babies off breastfeeding; if they are given a dummy when newly born, they would rather suckle on that than take a feed from their mum. Whether this is the case or not, it's probably wise to wait until you've established a breast-feeding routine before giving your baby a dummy, just in case there's a chance it could prevent him from wanting to breastfeed.

Thumb-sucking

A comfort habit that is very common in young children is thumb- or finger-sucking. As with using a dummy, it has the benefit of helping a child get to sleep at night and soothing him generally. Indeed, many children find it hard to fall asleep without sucking their thumb. This comfort habit is usually associated with babies and toddlers, although some children do continue into their teenage years. As with other comfort habits, thumb-sucking isn't indicative of a problem; it doesn't mean your child is traumatized in any way and should not therefore be a major cause for concern.

There are those who believe that prolonged thumb-sucking could cause a child's teeth to stick out. Obviously, your child has milk teeth until the age of five or six, so if he sucks his thumb in the early years it isn't likely to cause him any long-term damage. If, however, he continues to suck his thumb on a regular basis after his adult teeth have come through, there is a chance that it could make him bucktoothed. Therefore it's advisable to discourage your child from thumb- or finger-sucking after the age of six. It's likely, anyway, that he will grow out of this habit once he goes to school, especially if his friends aren't fellow thumb-suckers, as he won't want to feel like the odd one out.

Mum's top tip

If yours is a 'sucky' baby, then I don't see anything wrong in letting him suck either his thumb or a dummy. It's important for a child to learn to soothe himself and is unlikely to do any damage or affect how his teeth grow. And if you're really worried and think your little one will never stop sucking his thumb, think about how many adults you know who suck theirs – none? I thought so!

Toys and blankets

Other popular comfort objects include a favourite toy or blanket. And teddies aren't necessarily reserved for children... Hands up those proud owners of well-loved teddies which are falling apart at the seams and still live in bed with them? Young children are often inseparable from their teddies and insist on taking them everywhere. A teddy bear can act as a constant in a child's life – a faithful friend that is cuddly and familiar and doesn't answer back! Having a comfort habit such as this, far from being an indicator that your baby is lacking in anything, might actually increase his confidence, helping him to feel happy and secure.

How do I wean my child off a comfort habit?

If your child has reached the age of three or four and you're trying to wean him off his favourite comfort habit, there are a few tried and tested methods which might help:

top tips

- Reward charts. You could suggest to your child that for every night he sleeps without his dummy, he gets a star or smiley face on his chart.
- If your child is missing his favourite blanket or the comfort of sucking his thumb, give him lots of cuddles and affection.
- It's not a good idea to promise to buy him toys or presents to make up for his loss, as you don't want to resort to bribery. Think up some other reward instead, such as a trip to the playground or an outing to the local pool.

What are the benefits of sleep aids?

In an ideal world, your baby would go to sleep on his own. The reality, however, is that he might need a bit of help. And this is where sleep aids come in.

Sleep aids could be said to cover a wide range of things, from breastfeeding or swaddling your newborn baby (see pages 74–7) to traditional cuddly toys or modern products such as motorized cradles or bassinets that rock your child to sleep.

Also in the latter category are nightlights. These give off a nice warm glow which can help your child to get to sleep in the first place and which mean that the room isn't pitch black if he wakes up in the night, so that he's likely to feel happier about going back to sleep.

Other sleep aids include musical mobiles, which young children often find soothing and therapeutic. The colours of the mobile and the music can help lull your baby to sleep, acting in much the same way as a lullaby.

Teddies and cuddly toys, which also act as comfort objects, can be considered sleep aids as they do just that – help your baby to get to sleep. As with all comfort habits, don't worry that there's anything abnormal with your baby's behaviour if he needs one; on the contrary, it's perfectly natural and healthy.

Although sleep aids won't be effective for every child, they might work for you, so, if your child is having problems getting to sleep at night, it might be worth considering investing in one. Anything that serves to calm your baby down and help him (and you!) to have a peaceful night's sleep shouldn't be sniffed at!

Colic and sleep

If there's one thing guaranteed to keep your baby awake, it's colic. Colic can be one of the most trying things to deal with in the early months, testing your parenting skills and patience to the limit.

About 20% of babies get colic; it normally appears at around two to four weeks and can last for three months or longer. The good news is that it causes no harm to your baby (albeit a little distress) and does pass eventually. The bad news is that it is pretty intense while it lasts, involving recurrent bouts of unexplained crying for at least three hours a day and for a minimum of three days a week.

While there are many theories about why colic happens, scientists still can't decide on one definitive cause. The main point to remember is that all babies cry because it's the only way of communicating in those first few months. The difference with colic is that babies will cry intensely for hours and hours and cannot be calmed down by the usual methods.

Mum's top tip

I found colic medicine very helpful and used it for my son for a couple of weeks when we thought he had colic. My midwife also showed me a different way to help him bring up wind than we were shown in hospital. After every ounce or two ounces of milk she said to lie him flat along or over our legs and leave him there for a couple of minutes (if he cried we were to give him his dummy) and then to raise him to a sitting position, supporting his back with our hand and keeping his head tilted slightly. The wind just came up really well by itself then and he had no further problems.

SYMPTOMS

The most obvious symptom of colic is that your baby will cry for excessively long periods of time. Although he will cry at any time of the day, it is usually worse in the evening (just when you are starting to feel tired too). Other symptoms can include babies lifting their heads up, a very red face, drawing their legs up to their tummies and passing wind. This is probably why colic has traditionally been linked to abdominal pain caused by wind. In addition, some babies find it difficult to eat and sleep and some clench their fists and generally look uncomfortable.

HOW LONG DOES COLIC LAST?

All babies are different and some can have bouts of colic that don't last for long, while others can have symptoms of colic for up to three or four months, which can be very frustrating for parents. Health professionals agree that colicky babies are perfectly healthy and continue to thrive as well as babies who do not suffer from colic.

WHAT CAUSES COLIC?

The jury is still out when it comes to knowing what causes colic and while there are plenty of theories, nothing has been conclusively proven. Some experts think it is a digestive problem associated with abdominal gas; others think it is due to overfeeding, underfeeding or being handled too much. An immature nervous system has also been blamed, making your baby more sensitive to his environment. Because of this, he can find it difficult to process all the new sights, sounds and experiences throughout the day, culminating in a release of energy and a crying bout at the same time each evening.

Top tips for soothing a colicky baby

Because there are so many possible causes of colic, it is very difficult to find a single cure. Hence different parents report different methods for helping their colicky baby.

- Your baby may be calmed down with a rocking motion, either in your arms, in a sling, or even going for a journey in your car where the motion of travelling can be soothing.
- Your baby may cry less when she is swaddled as the physical constriction reminds her of when she was in the womb, making her feel more secure. It is also thought that swaddling your baby presses slightly on her abdomen, helping to relieve the painful build-up of gas that may be present. (For more on swaddling your baby, see pages 74–7.)
- Baby massage may also help, especially rubbing her tummy in an anti-clockwise motion (digestive systems work anti-clockwise, so it is important to rub in that direction).
- Giving your baby a dummy or letting her suck her thumb may help to soothe her (see pages 150–52).
- Giving your baby a change of scenery may help, so take her for an evening stroll. Removing all colourful toys and other stimuli may help if she is finding it difficult to process information she is learning. Try winding her down in the evening: maybe read her a bedtime story or rock her in your arms as you sing to her or play gentle music. Turn the lights low so that she's no longer distracted, and hence over-stimulated, by her surroundings.

top tips

- Try giving her a bath. Most babies love the bath and will be soothed by the warm water and being able to kick around nappyless for a while.

- Consider colic medicine. Certain products on the market are designed to give relief for colic, although they don't work for every child. Ask your pharmacist or health visitor for further advice about these products.

- Think of changing your diet. Some experts agree that a mother's diet can make colic worse if she is breastfeeding, so, if you are breastfeeding, try cutting out products that contain caffeine, such as coffee, tea and chocolate, and avoid orange juice, cabbage, onion and spicy foods. This is because your baby's digestive system is still very immature and she is unable to break down some of the proteins found in breast milk, possibly making it uncomfortable for her.

- Try soothing sounds. Many parents report their babies being calmed by music or monotonous sounds like the vacuum cleaner, white noise on the radio, or the washing machine.

At eight weeks old, my little girl started crying uncontrollably between and after all her feeds. She was able to bring wind up most of the time but seemed to be in pain regardless. I found it really difficult to watch her in so much pain. In the end, I went to see my health visitor who advised me to put drops in her milk, give her water to drink in addition to her milk and to massage her tummy in a circular motion before feeding her, putting my hands under her ribs and massaging her tummy downwards.

It is worth remembering that babies can cry uncontrollably for reasons other than colic; so always check with your GP first to rule out anything more serious.

Cranial osteopathy and colic

When a baby is born, her journey down the birth canal can be stressful as she twists and squeezes to get out. Her head is remarkably pliable and her bones may temporarily overlap to assist her entry into the world. As a result, your baby may have experienced some uncomfortable stresses within her body during the birth process.

One theory about the cause of colic is that, along with other parts of your baby's body, the nerve to her stomach can become compressed during birth and hence cause problems with digestion. Stress from a fast or difficult birth can also cause uncomfortable wind in the digestive tract.

Cranial osteopathy may help your baby as light pressure is applied to her head to assist her body in releasing any stresses and strains. It will not hurt your baby and should only be performed by a registered cranial osteopath. Parents have reported their babies sleeping much better after a session and often for much longer. Your baby may need a series of sessions, depending on her symptoms.

Cranial osteopathy can also help with a variety of childhood illnesses, including ear infections, asthma, and sinus and dental problems. If you are interested in learning more about this type of treatment, you can contact the General Osteopathic Council for more information. Alternatively, talk to your GP or health visitor as they should have information about registered cranial osteopaths in your area.

Top tips for coping with a colicky baby

Colic can be hard for parents to deal with, especially since the symptoms seem to peak around early evening and your baby's bedtime, when you and your partner are probably feeling frazzled, hungry and exhausted.

Here are **gurgle's** top tips on getting through this difficult time:

- Remember that colic does not usually last for long and for most babies the symptoms will stop after about three months.
- Your baby is not crying to annoy you or because you are a bad parent, or have done anything wrong. Try not to blame yourself and instead focus on helping to relieve your baby's symptoms.
- Try to share a bit of the burden with your partner or a friend or relative to give yourself a break once in a while. If your baby cries at roughly the same time each night, ask someone to pop in to help during this period to give you a break. Knowing when it's likely to occur, you can prepare yourself for it.
- Prepare some easy meals in the morning so you don't have to worry once your baby starts to fuss. Try to get some rest just before early evening to refresh yourself before the crying starts. You know its going to happen, and even if your baby seems inconsolable, he will feel comforted just by having you there even if he takes a long time to settle.
- Forget being the perfect housewife/wife/partner and leave the housework until another time. When this period is over you can go back to multi-tasking!
- Try not to take it out on your partner. Having a colicky baby isn't his fault any more than it is yours and you will need each other for support during this time. Take it in turns to deal with the crying so that one of you always has some time off.

top tips

top tips

- If things get too much, lay your baby down somewhere safe, such as in his cot (placed on his back) or pram, and go into another room to calm down. Put on your favourite music for a bit, and remember, this is very short period in your baby's childhood and it WILL pass!

- If you find you cannot cope with your baby's crying sessions, see your GP or mention this to your health visitor. They can give you advice and put you in touch with other healthcare professionals or parents who can help.

Baby, please stop crying...

If you are experiencing what the experts term excessive crying – that is, if your baby cries for long periods of time without respite – you should seek help.

It is extremely wearying, not to mention upsetting, for you as a parent to have to cope with a baby who cries relentlessly, at all times of day, but it is especially difficult to cope with during the night, when you feel that everyone in the world, with the exception of you and your baby, is slumbering deeply.

To help you deal with the situation, it is important to seek the support of a partner, relative or healthcare professional. In the meantime, here are some possibilities that may account for why your baby is crying:

- It could be that your child is just 'one of those babies'. Some children do seem to cry more than others and for apparently inexplicable reasons. This can be put down to the trauma of being newly alive. Truly! The bewildering array of new sights, smells and sounds filling your baby's eyes, nose and ears can contribute to a sensory overload. Think about how overwhelming it is to visit a country in which you don't speak the language, and how exhausted you feel at the end of a day spent exploring, and you might be able to empathize more with what your baby is going through as she adapts to the world around her.

- Some babies are extremely sensitive to changes in their environment. It is worth asking yourself if these extended crying periods are brought on at bath time, for instance, after being taken out of warm water. Try to establish a link between your baby's tears and sudden alterations in her environment, such as changes of temperature or being undressed. This could account for her upset.

- Sometimes, colic is used to explain bouts of excessive crying. Colic (see pages 156–63) is an umbrella term for crying without an apparent cause. Most people believe that a stomach upset of some description causes it, and some babies are indeed prone to more wind and stomach troubles than others, so this could be the case.

- In fact, in young babies (less than a few months old) a condition known as gastro-oesophageal reflux (or GOR) may occur due to the baby's as yet undeveloped digestive system. Stomach acid and other undigested stomach contents are pushed back up the baby's throat. This results in vomiting and indigestion-type pain for the baby. Usually, infants grow out of this and the symptoms are not very severe. If you are at all worried and your baby seems unduly upset by the condition, you should seek medical advice.

Mum's top tip

It took me a while to work this out but I realized that my baby had different cries depending on what the problem was. I trained myself to listen to the cry, to try to identify what was wrong – tired, hungry, bored, frustrated – and was surprised to find out how soon I could troubleshoot the problem. Even now, with other people's children, I can spot a tired baby cry when I hear one!

- If your baby had a very difficult or traumatic birth, this is often cited as a reason for excessive crying. Many parents have reported 'miraculous' results from visiting cranial osteopaths in order to solve this issue. The idea behind cranial osteopathy is that the practitioner will help to release the stresses held within the baby's head (and subsequently her body) by using non-invasive osteopathic techniques. (For more on this, see page 161.)

- If you are experiencing additional stresses – postnatal depression, bereavement, moving house, relationship break-up – it is likely that your baby is picking up on your tension. It then becomes an ever-perpetuating circle: you are upset and tense because your baby is crying and she is upset and tense because she can feel you are.

It is important that you seek help in these situations, if only for your peace of mind. If you are supported by those around you, it will be much easier for you to manage. If you are worried about your feelings or would like further advice on this topic, you could contact Cry-sis (see page 216–17 for contact details).

How diet can affect your baby

Remember that crying is really your baby's only form of communication with you. She doesn't yet have the skills or resources to deal with anything on her own, and things that seem inconsequential or minor trifles to us are worrying and scary for your newborn.

Diet does seem to have an impact on your baby's wellbeing. If you are breastfeeding, remember that your diet will have a knock-on effect on your baby. If you have eaten a spicy curry, this will go through into her milk and possibly upset her stomach. Likewise, if she is eating solids, new foods should be introduced one at a time, to establish whether they affect her negatively or not. If a food doesn't agree with your child, then the only way that she can show her discomfort is through her tears. Attending to her needs does not mean you are spoiling your baby.

What if my baby's overtired?

If your baby is overtired he will almost certainly start to cry as babies find being tired quite overwhelming. Sometimes they get themselves worked up into such a state that they cannot stop crying, especially when the reason they started crying in the first place was due to needing a sleep. Also, bear in mind that babies are taking in so much information and learning so many new things all the time that they need lots of sleep to recharge their minds and bodies.

You will usually be able to tell that he is tired as you will have come to understand what his crying means at different times. Even when you know what the problem is, you may not be able to address it immediately. Responding to your baby's crying as soon as you can is worthwhile, however, as it can nip a crying episode in the bud.

Soothing a fretful, tired baby can be a daunting task if you are unsure what method you should employ. The good news is that there are many effective ways to dry up those heart-wrenching tears. So, for those occasions when you need to soothe your tired, tearful baby, here are some tried and tested methods.

top tips

Top tips for overtired babies

- If your baby is tired and crying for this reason, then make sure you can put him down to sleep somewhere safe and comfortable. This could be a cot, buggy or even a sling.
- Respond to your baby's tears as soon as possible. This does not mean you are 'spoiling' him, as some people suggest. In

fact, research has proven that babies who feel secure develop faster. If you leave him to cry, he will feel insecure and confused.

- Put on some calming music (possibly music you played when he was in the womb), the radio or even the television. The noise may provide a big enough distraction to halt the crying.

- Cuddle your baby. Hold him in your arms and rock him. Babies love to be rocked as it transports them back to the safety and movement of being inside the amniotic sac.

- Reassure your baby by talking to him in a calm voice. If you become stressed, he will pick up on your tension and you could make it worse.

- Singing to your baby is usually a big hit. Don't worry if you are tone deaf; any lullaby you sing to your baby will sound like beautiful music to his ear. He loves the sound of your voice.

- Brightly-coloured toys, rattles, cloth books and mobiles may distract and calm your baby, but if you suspect he is overtired, he may well feel overstimulated by these and increase the volume of his complaint.

- Sometimes, putting a baby in his pushchair and going for a quick walk can be the answer. Likewise, certain babies just love to sit in a bouncy chair or cradle, being rocked to sleep.

- If you really cannot soothe your baby to sleep, a drive around the block in the car may help.

Teething and sleep patterns

As with other developmental milestones, teething can disrupt your baby's newly-established routines. This can be frustrating but it is an inevitable part of the development process. It may only last for a short time, and sort itself out, or you may need to try again to implement a good sleeping regime.

The reason that your baby's sleep patterns become disturbed is due to the discomfort he is in. The symptoms of teething are unlikely to occur before he is about four months and in some cases the first tooth won't emerge until a child is a year old. Your baby may become uncharacteristically grumpy or clingy but without showing any other signs of illness. This may begin a few weeks before a tooth even appears, so even if there is nothing to show for it, it could well be teething pain that is upsetting your baby.

Top teething tips

top tips

- Look out for swollen or red gums (plus a new passion for chewing) and a constant dribble. A bright red spot on one of his cheeks may also appear.
- The best course of action is to give him lots of cuddles and comfort. He may want to feed more often than usual and this is perfectly OK. You can buy teething rings that can be chilled in the fridge or freezer to help soothe those hot little gums. There is also a range of teething gels or homeopathic remedies that may help.
- If your baby has a temperature, you should consult your GP or health visitor for the best remedy. Remember that infant paracetamol must not be taken before the age of three months. Consult a GP, pharmacist or homeopath for more advice.

Phasing out co-sleeping

If you have been co-sleeping with your baby, then as she grows older there will come a time when you will decide she should move, at least into her own cot, and possibly into her own room. Bear in mind that current advice recommends that babies sleep in the same room as their parents for at least the first six months of their lives.

Even though co-sleeping can be very rewarding, for both parent and child, at some point you are going to want to have a bit of physical and mental space from your child. One of the negative aspects of co-sleeping is that your partner may feel a little left out, especially if you are breastfeeding. Having a little person between you in the bed can seriously inhibit any intimacy between you and your partner, and lovemaking will probably have become a thing of the past. Not only can your sex life suffer, but, as your baby gets stronger, diagonal sleeping positions and an ability to kick like a donkey may keep you or your partner awake during the night.

g For the **gurgle** video on **Co-sleeping**, go to **gurgle.com** and click on **Videos**

Mum's top tip

Our baby slept in our bed for the first few weeks after we came back from hospital. I found it really comforting to have her close to me, but my husband felt differently. To break the habit, each night we put her into a Moses basket that we moved further away from our bed, but still in our room; and gradually we moved it out of our room and into the nursery and put it in the cot. It was me who had to be weaned off co-sleeping as much as my baby!

Top tips for stopping co-sleeping

The best time to start this move out of your bed is when your baby is younger, rather than older. The longer you leave it, the harder it's going to be to wean your baby off her routine.

- As a transitional phase, a tried and tested solution can be for your baby to sleep in a cot (or something similar), placed right next to your bed and at the same height.
- As your baby becomes used to this arrangement, you can start to move the cot away from the side of your bed. The important thing is to make sure the place where she is going to sleep at night, on her own, is comfortable and familiar.
- If you haven't already done so, you should put your baby in the cot to play, or for daytime naps, so that she feels secure in her sleeping environment.
- Eventually, you can move your baby into her own room. Spending a lot of time in the room you want your baby to sleep in, especially during the bedtime routine, can also help her to feel comfortable and relaxed. Some parents wait in the room with their baby until she falls asleep, while others prefer to leave the room.
- Health visitors and other experts frequently frown upon staying with your baby as she falls asleep, as it is seen as making a rod for your own back. The logic behind this argument is that if your baby needs you around in order to fall asleep, she will expect you to be there and if she wakes up during the night, she won't be able to fall asleep without this 'association' – that is, you! At the end of the day, however, it is up to you to find out what works best for you and your child.

top tips

Holiday sleeping arrangements for your baby

Travelling with a baby, be it long haul or a weekend away, can inflict panic on many a level-headed parent.

Unless you're taking your baby backpacking in the Andes (unlikely), then you can usually find anything you've forgotten for junior at either the airport or the local supermarket. Babies are usually fairly adaptable when it comes to a new brand of nappies or shampoo.

One thing that's slightly more difficult to deal with is the sleeping arrangements. When you get to your hotel room, the first thing you do (now that you're a parent) isn't worry about the view, the size of the bed or the cost of the mini bar. No, the first thing you do these days is look frantically around for the cot ('But I booked it, I'm sure!'), spend 20 minutes trying to put it together if it's been left in the wardrobe, and then think: 'It's too small/big/different to what my baby is used to.' The answer may be to invest in a travel cot.

Travel cots

If you travel a lot in the car and regularly stay overnight at relatives' and friends' houses, then a travel cot is a good idea. Along with a lot of baby paraphernalia, these aren't cheap, of course. And there are a lot to choose from.

One of the biggest issues is weight. Some travel cots can weigh up to 16kg (35lb) – if you're planning on taking one on a plane, that's pretty much most of your baggage allowance gone. That said, these are generally the all-singing, all-dancing models that come with an adjustable bassinet space (a higher bit for your baby to sleep in) and a nappy-changing table. For most nights away, you can probably make do with changing your baby on the floor or your bed, and doing without a bassinet. Choosing a cot without all the trimmings will save on both weight and money.

There are some nifty travel cots on the market which weigh only about 2.5kg (5½lb). These don't have the regular four straight sides and are more like little pop-up tents. For tiny babies, you can get very lightweight travel cots that come in at less than a kilo (2lb). But these will only really last a few months as they are pretty much the same size as a Moses basket.

Some travel cots have two wheels at one end. This can be useful if you're getting your baby to sleep in one place (usually your bedroom) but want to put him in another room when you go to bed. When you have children, you are much more likely to book a hotel suite/apartment with more than one room. It's worth thinking about a travel cot with wheels as you may well want to put your baby to bed in the main room, moving him to a quieter room if you want to eat a meal or watch television without disturbing him.

The thing to remember about a travel cot is that it's never going to be the same as your child's cot at home. But as long as it's safe, secure and has no holes in the netting in the sides for little fingers and arms to get trapped, it'll do the job. Make sure you pack some familiar bedding to help your baby feel at home. And do bring spares – babies seem to store exploding nappies specifically for times when you can't get to a washing machine. It's also worthwhile taking some cot sheets, as not all hotels provide them; baby sleeping bags; and your child's favourite sleep toy. Anything that brings a bit of home comfort to bedtime is welcome.

Holiday routine

As hard as you think it might be, a normal routine can be pretty easy to stick to on holiday. It's not always necessary to take your baby back to your room for daytime naps. If you're on the beach, a pop-up UV-protector tent is a fantastic place for him to kick around in – and sleep. If your baby is in a routine, a change of scenery probably won't affect that, so assume he'll sleep when he usually does.

The one thing that can put routines out of kilter is a massive time difference. Luckily, babies don't really get the concept of jet lag, so do your best to stick to local time as soon as you arrive, and whatever time your body clock is on, aim to get your child to bed at the right time locally. You'd be surprised how adaptable young children are. Usually after one night they slot into local time, which is a lot quicker than most adults.

If you've got a long journey ahead, whether in the car or on a plane, the chances are your baby is going to sleep for a fair amount of it. There are two ways to look at this. Either: 'The baby's had far too much sleep, and won't go down tonight at the right time and I'll be up with him until at least 11.' Or: 'The baby's quiet; I don't have to worry about keeping him amused and the other passengers don't hate me.' But it's your call. Sometimes your baby will stay awake for an entire night flight, fall asleep just as you're about to get off, wake up and then have a nap that seems to keep him going. Or he may sleep through the entire journey and still have a perfectly decent night's sleep at the other end. The best thing to do with any long journey is assume he won't go to sleep and make sure you have enough books, toys and food to keep him occupied.

If you are travelling with your partner, make a deal that if you do a night flight with an awake baby, he does a full 24 hours' duty tomorrow, with no excuses!

Toddlers and sleep

Your toddler at 18 months

Most toddlers can walk fairly well by 18 months, though your heart may miss a beat as your child breaks into a run.

With running also comes the danger of roads, so it is very important that you teach your toddler road safety from the start. This means letting her know the boundaries; running is fine in the park, for instance, but not by the road. You'll need to keep her in sight at all times. Some overeager toddlers may need harnesses when out for a walk to stop them from dashing across the road.

With running and independence comes the ability to get lost. Children this age are too young to be taught what to do if they become separated from you, but you can sew their name into their clothes or onto a rucksack so that the information is there if needed.

NEW SKILLS
Acquiring new skills is fascinating for your toddler, but sometimes tiring for you as she practises building a tower over and over again. If you've read her favourite book 20 times and feel frustrated, don't despair. This is how your toddler learns about the world, by repeating what she has learnt and learning from her mistakes. Bear with her and if you can't handle reading it to her again, perhaps go for a walk together instead.

DAYTIME NAPS
Just when you'd got your toddler to stop stirring at night you're faced with the question of daytime naps. Some toddlers will have dropped from two naps to one a while ago, but if yours hasn't, it might be time to wean her down to one. If your toddler fusses more at bedtime or is reluctant to go down for the second nap, it might be time to change. Try moving her nap forwards by ten minutes every morning until your toddler is used to taking just one nap at around the middle of the day. (For more information, see page 124.)

Your guide to sleep routines: 18–24 months

After all those sleepless nights it may seem almost impossible to believe it, but by the time your toddler reaches two he will have spent more of his life asleep than awake. And even when he does turn two, he still needs far more sleep than an adult.

An energetic toddler usually needs a substantial amount of sleep – around 12–14 hours in any 24-hour period. But bear in mind that every toddler is an individual, and while some will thrive on just eight hours sleep a night, others may need 16. Also, if your child didn't sleep a great deal as a baby, the painful truth is he probably won't sleep much as a toddler – sorry!

Mum's top tip

My 18-month-old toddler started to take between 45 minutes and an hour to get to sleep. We hadn't changed the routine or done anything particularly different. I just couldn't understand what it was all about. Then I finally twigged: the clocks had gone back the previous weekend, so it was much lighter in the evening – my son thought it was still time to play, not to sleep. Blackout curtains swiftly followed!

Naps

Between the ages of 18 and 24 months, your toddler's nap times will probably decrease to one a day and last about one to two hours. Naps should not occur too close to bedtime as they may delay sleep at night. Children, like adults, have biological clocks and will become used to being awake and sleeping at the same time each day. The more consistent you are with your toddler's nap times and bedtime, the more likely he is to fall asleep without too much fuss.

Offering a choice

Toddlers crave independence and so offering them a choice rather than issuing a demand can make the difference between a smooth transition to bed and a full-blown tantrum. The optimum time for a child of 18–24 months to go to bed is around 7pm, and the optimum time for getting up between 6.30 and 8am. So, rather than saying to your child, 'It's bedtime now,' phrase it as a choice instead: 'Do you want to go to bed now or in five minutes?' Either way, you can't lose and your toddler will feel as if he has had a say in the matter. You could also ask your child what pyjamas he would like to wear or which bedtime book he would like to read.

Getting to sleep

By this age, your child should be able to drift off by himself without you having to stay and soothe him to sleep. If you do rock or sing him to sleep, you could be storing up problems for yourself as, when your child wakes up in the night, he will be dependent on having you there to get off to sleep again, and it's a rare toddler who sleeps more than six to eight hours at a stretch.

Your toddler at 24 months

Congratulations – this month your toddler has turned two! She has come a long way since this time last year when she was practically still a baby.

Now she can make herself understood in a basic way, she can stack blocks in order of size and she knows that a car is something you travel in to get to Granny's. She understands concepts such as hot and cold or high and low, and her memory has improved so much that she can remember in detail things that happened recently (such as your promise to give her sweets two days ago!). She can also be affectionate and shows a remarkable sense of humour – as well as having the odd temper tantrum.

NEW SKILLS

By her second birthday, your toddler will probably be able to point to specific pictures in books if you ask her ('Where is the little fish?', etc). She may be able to do a range of activities such as walk well alone, run, zigzag and dodge out of the way. She can go sideways, backwards and can stand up and sit down very quickly. She can probably jump and skip about and use her growing coordination to get what she wants (opening the door using a handle, or unscrewing the lid of the jam!).

TODDLER-PROOFING

Toddler-proofing your home is essential, as your child will soon learn the tricks you used to keep her out of trouble when she was a baby. Store medicines and cleaning products up high or in a locked cabinet and do the same with your bottles of beer and wine. Child locks on fridges and kitchen cupboards can also be useful, although a determined toddler may be able to undo a latch. If this is the case, a stair gate blocking off hazardous rooms may be required. It might be a good idea to stock up your first-aid kit and learn a bit of children's first aid to prepare for the inevitable cuts and grazes that lie ahead.

Your guide to sleep routines: 24–36 months

At two to three years old, your toddler will still require between 11 and 12 hours sleep a night, although his daytime nap might be shorter (on average one hour), and if he has been having two naps a day up until this point, he will most likely only require one.

If your toddler doesn't want to nap, don't force the issue, but do make sure he has some quiet time, for example, by reading with him. This will give him some downtime from the rest of his active day. Between 18 and 36 months, the optimum time for going to bed remains 7pm, getting up between 6.30 and 8am.

Toddlers experience much more REM sleep (rapid eye movement sleep during which they are more likely to dream – see page 14) than adults, moving from one sleep phase to another more regularly, which makes it much more likely that they will wake up. That's why it's so important that your toddler learns how to soothe himself back to sleep.

When my son Oliver hit two years, he really started to develop as a strong character, with definite likes and dislikes. I found the best way to continue to have happy bedtimes was to offer him a choice whenever possible. I'd present two options, both of which I was happy with, such as which of two toys to have in the bath or which of two bedtime stories to read. That way, we both felt we were in control.

Happy bedtime tips for toddlers

Getting your increasingly strong-minded toddler to bed may be more of a struggle than when he was younger, but here are **gurgle's** top tips on how to make the process easier:

- Ensure your toddler's bedroom environment stays the same every night: use the same nightlight and keep it in the same place; always have the curtains closed; don't move his bed around.
- Keep to a daily sleep schedule and a consistent bedtime routine.
- Try to keep to the same schedule every night – for instance, no more than 30 minutes from when your two-year-old gets out of the bath to the time he is tucked up in bed.
- Don't fret if your toddler becomes dependent on a comfort object such as a blanket or stuffed animal; if it gives him comfort, allow him to have it. (For more on sleep comfort habits, see pages 150–55.)
- Children this age love a bit more independence, so allowing your toddler to dress himself and choose the story you read will help keep him calm in the period before bed.
- Be firm with him if he wastes time getting into his pyjamas, explaining that it will mean less time for having a cuddle and reading a story.

top tips

Your toddler at 36 months

Congratulations! Your toddler turns three this month and the fun really begins. With the terrible twos (hopefully) behind you, you can look forward to a year in which your child has a greater command of his language skills and strives to be more independent. His imagination and creativity will grow stronger, too; he'll be able to paint, do puzzles, as well as run, jump and generally cause havoc.

NEW SKILLS

Your toddler may be able to dress himself this month. He now understands fairly complex concepts such as why he feels hot or cold, or why he has to wait for his dinner (you have to cook it!). As he turns three, he probably doesn't seem like a toddler any more as he can run, jump, hop, skip, balance and probably ride a tricycle. He can hold a conversation and most of the words he says can be understood. He is also developing a growing sense of independence. This month it's time to give yourself a huge pat on the back. You've come a long way since you gave birth and were given your tiny baby to care for.

For the **gurgle** video on **Toddler talking: how to help**, go to **gurgle.com** and click on **Videos**

The third birthday

The third birthday party is not that different from the second in terms of what your child can handle, and the same rules apply to both: keep it simple, don't invite too many friends and resist hiring magicians or party entertainers until your child is older. The difference this year is that you can include your child in the planning process. Ask him what kind of party he wants, but give him some limitations, or he might be upset when you tell him it cannot be held under the sea. If he does like the sea, make this a theme of the party, using foods, the birthday cake and under-the-sea decorations. Like two-year-olds, three-year-olds will get tired and grumpy after too much fun, games and cake, so keep the party small and the food healthy. Too much sugar will result in kids running riot.

Saying 'No'

You may notice your toddler starting to say 'No' back to you (it probably comes from hearing you say the word rather too often!). There are some children of this age who are really beginning to assert themselves and therefore say 'No' to pretty much everything! For young children, saying 'No' is a power trip, although once they have discovered they can use it, it can become very frustrating for you. Try to limit situations where your child can answer with a 'No'. For example, don't ask, 'Do you want to get dressed,' but instead say, 'What would you like to wear, your red top or blue one?' Changing how you phrase sentences can also help, so instead of saying, 'Go and put your shoes on,' try, 'Let's see who can put their shoes on the fastest, Mummy or Oscar.'

Choosing a bed for your toddler

At some point (usually around 30–36 months), you'll need to change the furniture again. Once more, your child will have outgrown a piece of kit – this time his cot – and now it's time for a bed. Some cots change into cot beds, which is good for your wallet as it means you can keep the same mattress and bedding, but most toddlers make the leap to a proper bed. Whether you get a toddler bed (and you can buy ones that can be extended into a regular single bed when your child is ready) or a proper three-footer is up to you, but bear in mind that if you opt for a full-size bed it means you can skip another transitional stage.

Buy a bed that's quite low to the floor so that if your toddler does happen to fall out, he won't injure himself. Also, think about getting a drop-down bed guard. Some children are still 'active' sleepers and get themselves into all sorts of positions at night, so the added security of a guard can mean a better night's sleep for all.

It's also worth splashing out on a decent mattress that will support your growing child.

Mum's top tip

I got a huge shock when my little boy learnt to climb out of his cot. I thought of putting a stair gate across the door so if he did get out of his cot he wouldn't be able to get out of his room, but my health visitor advised he would be safer in a bed and to let him get out of bed if he wanted to, just to make sure he was safe. So I put window locks on the windows and a stair gate across the door and made his room utterly dark so he couldn't see how to get out! Good for his eyes, too, or so I've heard.

When buying a new bed for your child, it's worth getting her involved. Let her pick out a new duvet cover (retina-burning pink with green flowers – not a problem if it gets her into bed) and let her help make up the bed. If you still have a cot, it's an idea to keep it in the room with her for the first few nights. At this stage, children can become so attached to things that just realizing the cot is no longer in the room can be incredibly upsetting. Make a big show of 'What a big girl you are now!' and, again, keep the routine as it was the day before. When bedtime comes, it's business as usual. Surprisingly, most children take to a new bed with few problems. They don't suddenly start getting up in the night, and they don't get out of bed and play with their toys when they think you can't hear.

Some children hate the dark and find a nightlight comforting, and they are useful for night-time trips to the toilet. When you first make the transition to a bed from a cot, it might be worth thinking of putting a safety guard at the top of the stairs as your child may be disorientated if she does get up in the night.

Dropping a nap

Somewhere between 24 and 36 months your child will almost definitely drop her daytime nap. You are allowed to be sad about this! Losing some precious time to yourself during the day after two years or so is tough. What's tougher is the fact that your little one will be getting really tired at about teatime, although feeding her should give her the energy to get through to bedtime without falling asleep on the sofa. There will be times when she still desperately needs a daytime nap and nothing will stop her, especially if she is in the car or buggy. Don't fret too much about this: it shouldn't stop her sleeping at night.

Top tips on moving to a bed

Three years is usually the time you'll transfer your child from a cot to a bed. Getting her to sleep in a bed shouldn't be too different from the transition to a cot (see page 137). Again, stick to the same routine and, fingers crossed, everything will carry on as normal. (For advice on when to move your child to a bed, see pages 196–7.)

- If your child does come to see you after she has been put to bed, gently and firmly say 'It's bedtime' and take her back, tuck her in and leave the room. If it happens again, do the same thing.

- Don't get engaged in conversation (if you give your child any opening for a bit of a bargaining, she'll be in there like a shot) and don't get to the stage where you think 'anything for a quiet life' and let her sit on your lap watching television for half an hour. Lapse even once and you will never be allowed to forget it! This is a good time to make sure you and your partner are absolutely clear on the routine for getting your child back to bed and you're not played off against one another.

- A nightlight can be comforting for some children, while others prefer pitch darkness. Keep a potty in your child's room when she has moved to a bed, as not all children want to walk to the bathroom on their own during the night.

For the **gurgle** video on **Potty training – where to begin**, go to **gurgle.com** and click on **Videos**

top tips

Troubleshooting: sleep and your toddler

Moving from cot to bed

Most parents start thinking about moving their child from a cot into a bed between the ages of two and three. By this age, he is probably outgrowing his cot and is capable of sleeping in a big bed without falling out and injuring himself, although to begin with you may want to fit a side protector to his bed to stop him falling out, particularly if he tends to move around a lot while asleep.

The first thing to consider before making the transition from cot to bed is whether your child is a good sleeper in his cot. If he still tends to wake in the night, then moving him to a bed will simply mean that he will now be up and about once he's awake – and probably trying to get into your bed too. Most experts agree that moving a child from a cot to a bed is unlikely to cure any existing sleep problems, and recommend trying to resolve these before making the change.

If your child is a poor sleeper, you might want to consider keeping his cot as a fallback if the night prowling gets too much. Sometimes, the threat of demotion to his 'baby cot' can work wonders in persuading him to stay in his bed and go to sleep.

Choosing the best moment

Before moving your child from a cot to a bed, consider what is going on in your child's life that might make such a transition stressful. Try and avoid making the switch at a traumatic time for your child – for example, when he's starting nursery or beginning potty training. Opt instead for a stress-free period and make it a positive thing – help him choose his duvet cover and sheets and get him involved in putting them on the bed for the first time.

Being evicted from his cot to make way for a younger sibling can work both ways: he might be delighted at his 'promotion' to a big boy's bed, but might equally yearn for the security of his babyhood cot, so don't automatically assume that it's a logical move which he will accept with equanimity. If you suspect he's not ready for the change, instead of buying a single bed straight away, consider investing in a cot bed, which can be transformed from a cot into a small, low-set bed.

If you do decide to buy a full-size single bed, look for models which are close to the floor with a firm mattress, and which will accommodate a side protector to stop your child falling out – a common hazard in the early days!

Coping with an early riser

While some children are happy to sleep in, it's fair to say that many toddlers love to get up at the crack of dawn and make the most of the day. The thought that by the time they reach their teens they will be sleeping until midday is scant consolation, however. So what can you do now to try and get a few more hours' sleep? The short answer is that there is no guarantee that any particular technique will work, but here are some suggestions.

GOING TO BED A LITTLE LATER

While in theory this ought to solve the problem, it's no guarantee that you will get a lie-in. You may find that your child wakes at the same time, regardless of when he went to bed, but is irritable as opposed to cheerful because he hasn't had his usual quota of sleep. Many children simply seem to be programmed to wake at the same time regardless of how much sleep they have had, and you may not be able to change this.

BLACKOUT BLINDS OR THICK CURTAINS

For those toddlers who tend to wake up when it gets light, installing a blackout blind and/or thicker curtains can often buy weary parents a bit more sleep, especially in the summer when it gets light earlier and dark a lot later.

CONTROLLED CRYING

For young children who are relentlessly early wakers, controlled crying (see pages 144–9) can help get them back to sleep, but depending on the time your child wakes, you may well end up just managing to get him off to sleep in time for you to get up, so the benefit may be minimal.

QUIET TOYS IN HIS COT OR BED

One technique which does work with many children is to put interesting but quiet toys in their cot or by their bed, to encourage them to play quietly once they wake up. Try putting cloth books and other interactive soft toys in easy reach, and rewarding your child for playing quietly by himself. Do remember that putting soft toys in the cots of young babies can pose a risk of cot death (or SIDS, see pages 48–53), so make sure you wait until your baby is at least 15 months old before you do this as well as checking the toys for small parts that he could choke on.

ALARM CLOCK

Many alarm clocks are now available that create gentle rings and sounds which are suitable for young children. Set the clock for a reasonable hour, and tell your toddler not to disturb you until the alarm has gone off. If he has enough to do in his room, you may find that this approach works well, and can even help him to tell the time later on.

Keeping your toddler happy

Giving your toddler a cuddle can halve the time she spends crying, according to researchers in a recent study.

Most parents hug their babies for about two and a half hours a day, but researchers claim that babies cuddled for five hours a day cry on average 50% less. The findings emerged after a month-long study of a hundred British parents by Wikinet. The research backs previous studies showing that cuddles release the feel-good hormone oxytocin, which helps to lower your stress levels.

For the **gurgle** video on **Toddler tantrums**, go to **gurgle.com** and click on **Videos**

Mum's top tip

I found my little girl's tantrums quite a difficult stage. If the tantrum was the result of frustration with her inability to master something or communicate her wishes, what seemed to work best was to be firm when explaining that her behaviour wasn't acceptable, while trying to support and encourage her at the same time. I tried to show her that with a little patience and perseverance, she could succeed.

Coping with nightmares

Nightmares happen when the brain processes and stores the information taken in every day and over-stimulating the mind. For a young child, all those new objects and experiences can reappear in his dreams in a frightening way – the book coming to eat him, the lampposts falling down around him…

Nightmares can occur when we are stressed, and while you think your toddler may have no stress in his life, consider whether there has been a big change recently – a new baby in the family, for example, or starting playgroup. If your child is having nightmares and you think it's due to stress, it's important to comfort him and reassure him that you love him, even if you don't know the precise cause of his anxiety. Probably the hardest thing for toddlers is that they cannot yet verbalize their fears or what is making them stressed, which can lead to a fair amount of frustration on their part.

That said, it's quite common for a young child to have nightmares that aren't due to stress, so don't be concerned that there is anything unusual about your toddler's behaviour. Similarly, don't blame yourself, thinking you've done something wrong; it's not your fault. There's no magic cure for nightmares: the best thing is just to reassure your child. Some children have nightmares only once in a while, others may have them more frequently; there's no set pattern.

Top tips if your child has a nightmare

- Go to him if he is upset, comfort him by giving him a cuddle, rubbing his back or stroking his temples.
- If he wants to talk about the nightmare, let him; it might help to make it go away.
- Reassure your child that it is just a bad dream and not real.
- Lie down with your child and, if he wants, let him fall asleep with you next to him.
- If he is really scared, it might be better to get into bed next to him, so you can prove to him his room is not scary and also to stop the habit of him coming into your bed when he is scared.
- Before your child goes to bed in the evening, reassure him that you are close by and that you love him.
- Buy some nightlights so that his room isn't pitch black.
- Don't let him eat dinner too late, especially anything sugary, so that he is not still digesting food when he settles down to sleep.

top tips

What are night terrors?

Some children experience night terrors, which are slightly different from nightmares. These occur when a child is roused from deep sleep in an utterly terrified state. But rather than waking completely, as with a nightmare, she may still appear to be asleep and will probably be fairly disorientated.

In such a situation, it's likely that cuddles will not help greatly as your child isn't really conscious of what is going on. Another difference between nightmares and night terrors is that, whereas with the former your child is likely to remember what happened, she may wake up the morning after experiencing a night terror with absolutely no recollection of what occurred.

- Between the ages of two and six, children become more prone to night terrors (although people of any age can experience them).

- Remember that night terrors are not the same as nightmares. If your toddler wakes in the middle of the night crying but consolable, she's probably had a nightmare.

- If she is hysterically crying, screaming and non-responsive, it is more likely she is in the throes of a night terror.

- There is very little you can do to stop or reduce a night terror. Despite appearing to be awake, a toddler experiencing one is actually in a very deep sleep pattern and will be unlikely to respond to calming words or cuddles.

- Try not to talk to or restrain your child – it could just make things worse. Instead, make sure she is safe (some children make a bolt from the bed in their fear) and sit with her until it passes. Remember that most night terrors last only a few minutes – although it will feel a lot longer!

WHAT CAUSES NIGHT TERRORS?

It's thought that being overtired is linked to night terrors. Encourage your toddler to have a nap (or naps) at the regular time in the day, and don't put her to bed too late or wake her too early.

If your child is running a fever or has recently been through a stressful situation, she may be more likely to experience night terrors.

TREATMENT

Some experts recommend interrupting your child's sleep cycle. This is accomplished by waking her up after about one to two hours (night terrors usually strike during the first half of sleep), or about 15 minutes before the time the night terrors usually occur. This change in her sleep pattern could be enough to ward off night terrors.

The only other advice is just to stay with your child and sit it out. Remember that night terrors are scarier for you than they are for your toddler – who will remember nothing about them the next day. If you are concerned about the frequency or duration of your child's night terrors, do speak to your GP or health visitor.

Coping with a sleepwalker

The reasons why some people sleepwalk are still a bit of a mystery, although sleepwalking seems to run in families. It can begin after your child starts to crawl, but at this stage she's likely to be in a cot so it won't be too much of an issue.

Most sleepwalking happens within an hour or two of falling asleep, when your child is deeply asleep. Sleeping in an unfamiliar place or having a high fever can cause a child to have a sleepwalking episode.

Your child may appear to be wide awake, and even have a conversation with you (which probably won't make much sense). If she can get out of bed, she might wander round the house, or think she's in the bathroom when she's in a cupboard, which could lead to little accidents happening.

TREATMENT

We've all been told this a hundred times but that doesn't mean it isn't true: you should never wake a sleepwalker unless he or she is in danger. If you can, just guide your child back to bed. She won't remember anything in the morning, so don't talk about it with her as it just causes her undue worry about going to bed. (Put yourself in her shoes: would you have liked to have been told at two or three years of age that you wander round the house in the dark?)

Make sure there are no toys or obstacles your child could trip over in her room if she does get out of bed, and put a stair gate at the top of the stairs, or even in the doorway of her room, so she can't wander around the entire house. Injuries can occur, but these are usually when a child has fallen downstairs or managed to get outside, so always make sure all doors and windows are locked shut at night. This is especially important when on holiday as an unfamiliar environment could trigger a bout of sleepwalking.

Mum's top tip

When my little girl started sleepwalking, I was terrified she would harm herself by bumping into something or falling down the stairs. I talked to the health visitor who reassured me it was a temporary phase and advised me to fit stair guards and to make sure that windows had window locks. Sure enough, the sleepwalking phase passed but the best advice I had was to make sure she was secure in her room and couldn't hurt herself.

Why does my child grind his teeth at night?

The horrific sound of teeth grinding can make people run screaming from a room – it's up there with nails down a blackboard. But it's a common night-time habit: three out of ten children will grind or clench their teeth, according to experts, with the highest incidence in children under five.

Most teeth grinding starts when children are about ten months old and their upper and lower front teeth have made an appearance. Some children will grind their teeth through the night, and others do it on and off.

There are several reasons why it happens. It may be a response to pain such as earache or teething. If your child is under any form of stress, it could also cause him to grind his teeth – even arguing with parents and siblings can cause enough stress to prompt teeth grinding or jaw clenching.

Children who are hyperactive may also experience teeth grinding.

TREATMENT

Although it may sound as if the teeth are actually wearing away, grinding doesn't actually damage them and most children outgrow the habit. If you're concerned about any damage it may be doing, mention it to the dentist next time you take your toddler. In cases of severe grinding, where the child's teeth are being damaged or his jaw or face is becoming sore, dentists may prescribe a special night guard, similar to the protective mouthpieces worn by rugby players.

Why is my toddler such a noisy sleeper?

If your child snores and has difficulty breathing (pausing for a few seconds while asleep), she might be suffering from sleep apnoea. Other signs of the condition are your child breathing through her mouth most of the time during the day, coughing a lot at night and being a restless sleeper. She may also wake up frequently during the night; this is due to her needing more air than she is getting, causing her to wake.

With sleep apnoea, the upper airways become blocked during sleep when the muscles of the body, including the tongue and throat, are in a relaxed state. In a young child, it's usually caused by enlarged adenoids or tonsils.

Sleep apnoea may also be caused by frequent illnesses related to the ears and throat. Ear infections, tonsillitis and sore throats can all lead to bouts of sleep apnoea. If your child is overweight or has a receding chin, she will also be more susceptible as either of these may make it difficult for air to reach her lungs when she is asleep. Sleep apnoea peaks between the ages of three and six, which is when tonsils and adenoids are at their largest in comparison to child-sized airways.

If you are concerned that your child might have sleep apnoea, her daytime habits will be another indicator. Children who suffer from the condition are usually sleep deprived, which makes them more irritable and frustrated. They might want to sleep more than usual during the day and they may not be able to control where or when they drop off.

Worryingly, a child with sleep apnoea might grow more slowly than other children as she won't be sleeping long enough to benefit from growth hormones released at night.

TREATMENT

If you suspect your child is suffering from sleep apnoea, talk to your GP. You may then be referred to an ear, nose and throat specialist to see if your child's tonsils or adenoids need to be removed. This is a simple procedure and usually rectifies the situation.

Mum's top tip

I was worried about my baby's noisy breathing at night. I consulted my GP and was reassured to learn that most parents who seek advice on a sleep-related problem report an improvement as their child gets older. Our consultation involved being referred to a specialist who took a full sleep history which was analysed, along with physical checks, to make a diagnosis. By 18 months, I'm delighted to report that the problem had disappeared of its own accord.

Dry at night

Being dry at night comes earlier to some children than to others. Bedwetting is normal and very common in pre-school age, especially among boys.

Night-time bladder control can be achieved any time between two and five years, but accidents can still occur after that. As long as it doesn't happen regularly, it shouldn't be a cause for concern. And remember, children do not wet the bed to be naughty; it's just that the message that the bladder is full hasn't yet managed to reach the brain and wake the child up. Bear in mind, too, that children's bladders are smaller and weaker than those of adults, so it's more difficult for them to hold urine; and some children just sleep too deeply to wake up if they need to go to the toilet.

Bedwetting usually sorts itself out by the age of seven or even a bit later. About one in seven children aged five and one in 20 children aged ten wet the bed. If you discuss it with friends who have young children, you'll probably be surprised at how many have the occasional mishap.

Bedwetting can also be linked to upheaval in a child's life – a new school, a new baby in the family, moving home or being bullied or struggling at school. It has also been linked to not being able to breathe properly when asleep due to blocked sinuses or related conditions (see sleep apnoea, pages 210–11).

TREATMENT

If your child is under six there really is no need to seek treatment as night-time bedwetting is something she will usually grow out of. If your child is older, try using disposable sleep-pants, which aren't as bulky as nappies and which will save you constantly having to wash her bedding. Place a protective undersheet on her mattress to keep it dry.

Holiday sleeping arrangements for your toddler

Travelling with a child, whatever his age, can be stressful. Now that your baby is a toddler, at least you no longer have to bring everything with you bar the kitchen sink. But some forward planning is still necessary, especially when it comes to sleeping arrangements.

When your little one gets a bit older, and a cot is too small for him, be prepared to freestyle with the furniture in your hotel or holiday apartment. A single bed on a marble floor can strike fear into the hearts of most parents, but just put the mattress on the floor and let him sleep on that. Place cushions or pillows around the sides in case he does roll around a bit.

It's difficult to know in advance what sort of temperature the room is going to be before you get there (will the air-con be icebox-cool or so noisy you have to switch it off and sweat the night away?). If your child is too hot, he can sleep in a nappy; too cold, it's long-sleeved pyjamas every night. Don't assume because it's a hot country the room will be hot to sleep in. If your child is cold, he'll wake up crying. And a holiday is supposed to be relaxing, right?

Top tips for travelling with a toddler

- Stick to your child's normal bedtime routine. It's worth taking a few bath toys with you, too, to make sure bathing is familiar.
- Read a book with your child before bed and tuck him in as you would normally.

- If there are shutters on the window, use them.
- If the curtains are really thin, it might be worth digging out one of those blankets that always lurk in the back of the hotel wardrobe by the safe and sticking it up over the window, student-digs style. It might look awful, but if it means your toddler will sleep in later than sunrise, it has to be worth it.
- If you're staying with friends or family, be blunt and say you need something to put up at the window or the whole house will be awake at dawn tomorrow. It's amazing what that sort of threat will do. There'll be a thoroughly blacked-out room waiting for you when you arrive!

Mum's top tip

You can give your toddler a lollipop to suck during takeoff and landing, some airlines provide these. I was lucky and breastfed my daughter until she was three, and that helps, or you could try a dummy if yours uses one. Apparently the sucking action helps to avoid that popping sensation due to changes in air pressure.

Resources

AIMS (Association for Improvements in Maternity Services)
For help obtaining maternity and postnatal care
0870 765 1433
www.aims.org.uk

BLISS Baby Life Support System
Support for parents of special care babies
0500 618 140
www.bliss.org

Contact a Family
Offers support to parents of children with special needs and disabilities
0808 808 3555
www.cafamily.org.uk

Cry-sis
Helpline for parents with crying and sleepless children
020 7404 5011
www.cry-sis.com

Dads UK
The first and only UK helpline for single fathers
07092 391489
www.dads-uk.co.uk

Daycare Trust
Provides information to parents, employers, policy-makers and providers
020 7840 3350
www.daycaretrust.org.uk

The Foundation for the Study of Infant Deaths
The UK's leading baby charity working to prevent sudden deaths and promote health
020 7233 2090
www.sids.org.uk

Gingerbread
Self-help organization for lone-parent families
0800 018 4318
www.gingerbread.org.uk

Home-Start
Provides support and friendship to parents of under-fives
0800 068 6368
www.home-start.org.uk

MAMA (Meet-A-Mum Association)
Offering invaluable sympathy and support from other mums
0845 120 3746
www.mama.co.uk

The Millpond Sleep Clinic
The international child sleep clinic
020 8444 0040
www.mill-pond.co.uk

National Association of Citizens Advice Bureau
Offers free advice on issues including pregnancy and employment
www.citizensadvice.org.uk

NCT (National Childbirth Trust)
Offering guidance on pregnancy, birth and parenting
0870 444 8708
www.nct.org.uk

NHS Direct
National helpline offering medical guidance and health information
0845 4647
www.nhsdirect.org.uk

Parentline Plus
Information and support for families
0808 800 2222
www.parentlineplus.org.uk

QUIT
Practical help to stop smoking
0800 00 22 00
www.quit.org.uk

Raising Kids
Support for anyone raising children of any age
020 8222 3923
www.raisingkids.co.uk

Relate
Provides couple counseling for those with relationship problems
0845 130 4010
www.relate.org.uk

TAMBA (The Twin and Multiple Birth Association)
Provides support for families of twins, triplets and more
0800 138 0509
www.tamba.org.uk

Index